HANDBOOK
OF
TRANSISTOR CIRCUITS

by Allan Lytel

HOWARD W. SAMS & CO., INC.
THE BOBBS-MERRILL CO., INC.
INDIANAPOLIS · KANSAS CITY · NEW YORK

FIRST EDITION

SIXTH PRINTING—1969

Library of Congress Catalog Card Number: 63-20742

PREFACE

The use of semiconductor devices in industrial applications is growing at a rapid rate. Indeed, although much attention is being given to how the devices already in production can be used in various types of industrial applications, current emphasis is on the development of new solid-state devices with specialized characteristics for specific applications. Because of the tremendous effort made in manufacturing and developing semiconductor devices, it is very difficult to keep up with the state of the art as actually used in industry. It behooves us, therefore, to stop and take a close look at what has happened in the last few years.

This book is a compilation of transistor and rectifier circuits used for a wide variety of applications. Naturally it is impossible to include all of the many such circuits in a single volume; instead, a selection of typical designs has been included. In each of the 13 different circuit categories, schematic diagrams, parts lists, and text discussions of the operation are given for a number of representative circuits. In one reference source this book provides material that otherwise would be available only from the various manufacturers.

Acknowledgement must be given to the following manufacturers, who supplied much of the data from which this book was prepared: Shockley Transistor, Transitron Electronic Corp., Sylvania Electric Products, Inc., General Electric Co., Motorola Semiconductor Products, Inc., Minneapolis-Honeywell Regulator Co., Solid State Products, Inc., Ferroxcube Corporation of America, Westinghouse Electric Corp., Radio Corporation of America, Crystalonics, Inc., and Eastman Kodak Co.

ALLAN LYTEL

CONTENTS

SECTION 1

SECTION 2

SECTION 3

SECTION 4

SECTION 5

SECTION 6

SECTION 7

SECTION 8

SECTION 9

SECTION 10

Three-Phase, Controlled-Rectifier Circuit for DC Power Supply—Pulse-Triggered Ignition Circuit—Constant-Voltage Power Supply —10-Ampere, 400-Volt Rectifier Tester—6-Volt Power Supply—12-Volt Power Supply—Portable and Silicon Rectifier Tester—Chopper-Controlled, Regulated Power Supply—Cascade-Amplifier Regulator — 1000-Watt Regulated Supply — 150-Watt Regulated Supply—Simple, Zener-Diode Voltage Regulators—Current Regulator—Series Voltage Regulator

SECTION 11

Latching Relay—Fire Alarm—Circuit for Geiger-Tube Radiation Detector—Geiger-Tube Radiation Detector—Sound-Operated Relay —Lead-Sulfide, Photoconductor Radiation-Detector Circuit—Relay Actuator—Automatic Garage Light—Rain-Alarm Circuit—Lamp-Dimmer Circuits—Induction Transceiver

SECTION 12

Power Oscillators-High-Power Pulse Generator With Dual Output —Theremin—Boat Horn—High-Voltage Sawtooth Generator—Model-Train Horn—Controlled-Rectifier Oscillator—Blocking Oscillator—Transistorized Organ—Phase-Shift Oscillator—Blocking Oscillator—Controlled-Rectifier Relaxation Oscillator—UJT Pulse Generator

SECTION 13

DC-to-DC Converter—42VDC-to-200VDC Converter—120-Watt, DC-to-DC Converter, DC-to-DC Power Converters—6VDC-to-12VDC Converter—12VDC-to-300VDC Converter—1-kc Chopper —DC Chopper—Inverter Charger—Inverter—DC-to-DC Converters

COUNTERS

FREQUENCY DIVIDERS

The four-layer diode (a PNPN device) can be used to make simplified frequency-divider circuits, such as those used for electronic organs. A master oscillator is used to generate the basic, or original, frequency (f), which, for example, can correspond to middle C. Output from this master oscillator is then used to synchronize a sawtooth oscillator that uses a four-layer diode. This produces a large-amplitude sawtooth about 30 to 40 volts whose frequency is the same as that of the master oscillator. If it is desired to produce C below middle C, it is necessary to divide the frequency by two, but the output should remain a sawtooth. The technique for doing this is as follows.

Diode D1 is a simple sawtooth oscillator which has a free-running frequency of just below ½ f, where f is the original oscillator frequency. However, sync pulses coming from the master oscillator are of the fundamental frequency (f). These pulses are adjusted in amplitude so that every other pulse triggers the four-layer diode (D1).

This circuit produces pulses across the series resistors in the path of the capacitor discharge. The 18-ohm resistor provides a pulse amplitude of the proper value. In turn, these pulses are fed to the next stage (D2) which produces an output of the original frequency divided by 4, since every second input pulse has sufficient amplitude to trigger the stage. Thus, in sequence the first stage produces an output whose frequency is the original divided by 2, the second is the original frequency divided by 4, the third is the original frequency divided by 8, etc.

A complete circuit that provides sawtooth-voltage outputs over

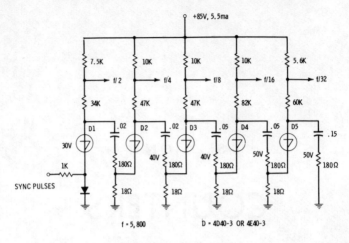

(A) Schematic diagram.

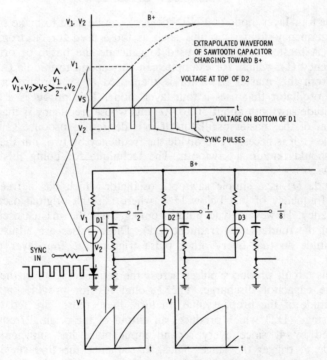

Courtesy Shockley Transistor, Unit Clevite Transistor.

(B) Waveforms.

Working organ circuit.

5 octaves is shown. Note that the component values are not similar for each stage, but they change as the frequency of the stage changes. Frequency control is obtained by varying the resistance and capacitance so that all of the diodes have the same switching voltage.

This frequency divider is free-running at incorrect frequencies if there is no sync pulse. It is necessary, therefore, to be sure that the original oscillator source signal is present and that each stage provides sync for the succeeding stages.

BINARY COUNTER 1

The binary counter uses a positive 3 volt, 1- to 10-μsec. input pulse to produce an output pulse that is either positive or negative, depending on which controlled rectifier is conducting when the input pulse is applied.

If controlled rectifier TCR1 is conducting, a 3-volt bias is developed across resistor R1 and applied to the cathode of diode D1 through resistor R2. When a positive 3-volt input pulse is applied to the junction of the anodes of diodes D1 and D2, the positive 3-volt bias on the cathode of D1 holds it at cutoff, and current flows through resistors R4 and R5 and diode D2. The current through R4 and R5 develops a positive voltage at the gate of controlled rectifier TCR2, thus gating TCR2 on. When TCR2 starts to conduct, the sudden presence of a positive voltage at the cathode of TCR2 produces a current through capacitor C2 and resistor R7. This current through R7 develops a positive pulse at the output. At the same time, when TCR2 starts to conduct, the sudden presence of a

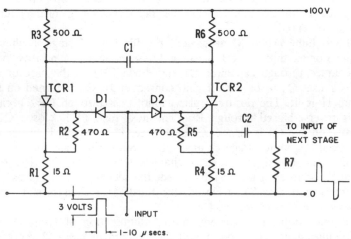

Courtesy Transitron Electronic Corp.

Binary-counter circuit.

9

negative-going voltage at the anode of TCR2 is coupled through capacitor C1 to the anode of TCR1, cutting TCR1 off. Now diode D2 is back-biased and controlled rectifier TCR1 is in the Off state. When the next 3-volt pulse is received at the input, current through resistors R1 and R2 and diode D1 develops a positive voltage at the gate of controlled rectifier TCR1, gating TCR1 on. TCR1 is now On, and TCR2 is switched Off through coupling capacitor C1. When TCR2 is switched to the Off state, its cathode suddenly goes to ground potential. The sudden decrease in voltage produces a current through capacitor C2 and resistor R7. This current through R7 develops a negative pulse at the output. Therefore successive positive input pulses result in alternate positive and negative pulse outputs that can be used to drive a binary readout system. Several of these binary counters can be combined to form a binary counter system.

BINARY COUNTER 2

The binary counter can be used by science or mathematics teachers to demonstrate binary addition or by students as part of a science fair display of computer-type circuits. The circuit may be operated by a relay, as shown, or with a photocell in place of S1. It can be used to count objects moving on a conveyor belt or the number of persons who pass by the photocell. The schematic diagram shows two sages, but the counter can be extended to as many stages as desired. The counter counts from 0 to $(2^n - 1)$, where n is the number of stages. For example, with two stages it will count to 3, with three stages it will count to 7, with four stages it will count to 15, and so on. The counter consists of cascaded flip-flop circuits containing indicator lights so that the state of each stage of the counter can be observed.

Each time switch S1 is closed, the flip-flop of stage 1 changes state. For example, if Q1 of stage 1 is conducting, a positive pulse is coupled through capacitor C1 and diode CR1 to the base of Q1. This causes Q1 to be cut off, and consequently, Q2 is turned on and lamp I1 is lit. The positive pulse cannot pass through CR2 because it is reverse-biased through R6. The next time S1 is closed Q2 is turned off and Q1 is turned on. Each time Q2 of stage 1 is turned on, the second counter stage changes state. Similarly, each time Q2 of stage 2 is turned on, stage 3 changes state. Thus the first stage changes state each time S1 is closed; the second stage changes state every second time S1 is closed; the third stage changes state every fourth time S1 is closed; and so on.

If one adopts the convention that illumination of lamp I1 of a particular stage represents 1 and illumination of lamp I2 represents O, then a conversion table from decimal to binary counting can be

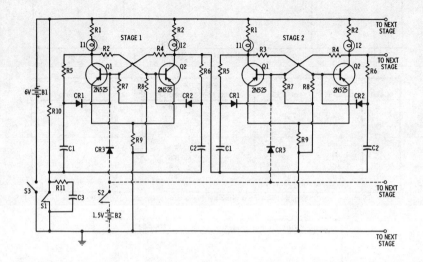

B1—6V. Battery, Burgess F4BP or equivalent.
B2—1.5V. Battery, Burgess #2R or equivalent.
C1, C2—.047 or .05 Mfd. Paper or Ceramic Capacitor.
C3—.1 Mfd. Paper Capacitor.
CR1, CR2, CR3—1N34A Diode.
I1, I2—Sylvania #48 or #49 2V., 60 ma. Pilot Lamp.
Q1, Q2—Sylvania 2N525 Transistors.
R1, R2—68Ω, ½w. Resistor.
R3, R4, R7, R8—1.2K ½w. Resistor.
R5, R6, R10—10K, ½w. Resistor.
R9—4.7Ω ½w. Resistor.
R11—27Ω ½w. Resistor.
S1—Switch, normally open momentary contact
     pushbutton type such as Graynill Type 2201

     or equivalent.
S2—Same as S1.
S3—S.P.S.T. Toggle Switch.
NOTE: C1, C2, R1 through R9, CR1, CR2, CR3, I1, I2,
       Q1, Q2 must be duplicate for each
       stage used.

Courtesy Sylvania Electric Products, Inc.
Two-stage, binary-counter circuit.

Count	Stage 1	Stage 2	Stage 3
0	0	0	0
1	1	0	0
2	0	1	0
3	1	1	0
4	0	0	1
5	1	0	1
6	0	1	1
7	1	1	1
8	pattern	repeats	

TABLE I—Binary representation of count (least significant digit on right).

Count	Stage 1		Stage 2		Stage 3	
	Lamp l1	Lamp l2	Lamp l1	Lamp l2	Lamp l1	Lamp l2
0	off	on	off	on	off	on
1	on	off	off	on	off	on
2	off	on	on	off	off	on
3	on	off	on	off	off	on
4	off	on	off	on	on	off
5	on	off	off	on	on	off
6	off	on	on	off	on	off
7	on	off	on	off	on	off
8	pattern	repeats				

TABLE II—Count display for 3 stage counter.

N (number of counter stages)	(2^N-1)
1	1
2	3
3	7
4	15
5	31
6	63
7	127
8	255
9	511
10	1023

TABLE III—Count capability as function of number of stages.

Courtesy Sylvania Electric Products, Inc.

made (Table I). In this table the count is given in its binary representation from right to left (least significant digit on right). Table II shows the count display for a three-stage counter, and Table III shows the highest count possible for various numbers of stages.

RING COUNTER

A ring counter may be considered as a circuit that sequentially applies voltage to two or more loads at a time. These may either be power loads or signal loads. In this circuit, controlled rectifiers SCR1, SCR2, and SCR3 form a three-stage ring counter. SCR4 is a reset pulse generator which is not required for all applications.

When power is first applied to the circuit, none of the SCR's are turned on. To set the circuit a positive pulse is applied to the set pulse input which applies a positive trigger to the gate of SCR1, switching SCR1 from the Off state to the On state and resulting

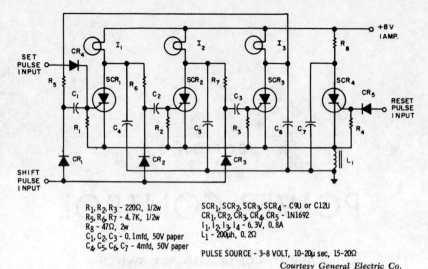

R1, R2, R3 - 220Ω, 1/2w
R5, R6, R7 - 4.7K, 1/2w
R8 - 47Ω, 2w
C1, C2, C3 - 0.1mfd, 50V paper
C4, C5, C6, C7 - 4mfd, 50V paper

SCR1, SCR2, SCR3, SCR4 - C9U or C12U
CR1, CR2, CR3, CR4, CR5 - 1N1692
I1, I2, I3, I4 - 6.3V, 0.8A
L1 - 200µh, 0.2Ω

PULSE SOURCE - 3-8 VOLT, 10-20µ sec, 15-20Ω

Courtesy General Electric Co.

Ring-counter circuit.

in current flow through lamp I1. Since SCR2 and SCR3 are in the Off state, their anode voltage is 8 volts, therefore reverse-biasing diodes CR1 and CR3. The cathode of CR2, which is connected to the anode of conducting SCR1, is at approximately 1 volt.

If a positive pulse with a peak amplitude of less than 8 volts and greater than 3 volts is applied to the shift pulse input, CR1 and CR3 block the pulse from the gates of SCR1 and SCR3, but the pulse is coupled through CR2 and C2 to the gate of SCR2. Thus, SCR2 is triggered on. Capacitor C5, which was previously charged through lamp I2, now discharges through SCR2 and inductor L1. The large voltage pulse developed across L1 reverse-biases SCR1, switching it off. Capacitor C4 holds the anode voltage of SCR1 down during the commutating interval. When successive shift pulses are applied, SCR3 is switched on and SCR2 is switched off, SCR1 is switched on and SCR2 is switched off, and so on in a similar manner. When a pulse is applied to the reset pulse input, SCR4 is switched on, and capacitor C7 discharges through SCR4 and L1, producing a large voltage pulse which reverse-biases whichever SCR is in the On state. SCR4 will continue to conduct until one of the other SCR's is switched on. Additional stages may be added to the circuit as desired. A ten-stage circuit using ten SCR's can be used to perform the function of a decade counter with direct lamp readout.

POWER CONTROL

REMOTE-CONTROLLED SCR SWITCH

The silicon-controlled rectifier (SCR), which has many versions, is used as a static and sensitive latching switch; it can be substituted for relays, contact cores, or other devices. Alternating current can be used for the power supply where latching is undesirable. The circuit arrangement shown can be used for the remote-control actuation of various types of low-power loads such as relays, alarm systems, bells, or warning lights. A single semiconductor controlled rectifier is shown with an AC input that can be in the 100- to 200-volt range. The gate of the controlled rectifier is adjusted to a positive bias just below the triggering level by means of R1, R2, and the diode CR1. In this example the antenna coil and trimmer are tuned to a specific frequency used for remote control, such as a frequency in the 27-mc

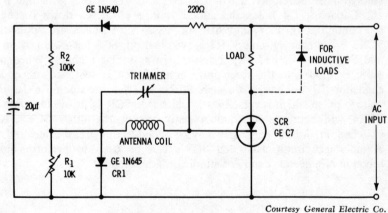

Courtesy General Electric Co.

Remote-controlled SCR switch circuit.

Citizens band; R1 is adjusted so that the controlled rectifier triggers when it receives the proper transmitted signal. The bias arrangement allows for a low resistance path for the leakage current.

In this circuit there is reasonable temperature compensation, since CR1 and the controlled rectifier are maintained at about the şame temperature. As a result a constant voltage differential exists between the steady-state bias voltage and the gate trigger voltage. If, however, the temperature of the controlled rectifier is raised to a sufficiently high value, the rectifier will spontaneously trigger. This temperature-triggering is put to practical use in other types of circuits.

A SOLID-STATE THYRATRON REPLACEMENT

A high-sensitivity controlled rectifier used as a controlled switch can be coupled with a rectifier in the circuit shown. This circuit acts like a thyratron in many ways, since it has a high signal-input impedance, low pickup and drop-out current, and can handle large amounts of power. In this circuit the grid, anode, and cathode connections for an equivalent thyratron tube are shown. With a

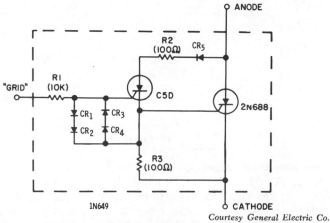

Courtesy General Electric Co.
Solid-state thyratron replacement circuit.

negative potential on the "grid" terminal, a stabilizing gate bias for the controlled switch is provided by CR1, CR2, and resistor R1. When the anode is positive and the grid is driven positive, the controlled switch starts conducting. This in turn triggers the larger controlled rectifier. Thus there is current flow from cathode to anode through the larger controlled rectifier. Diodes CR3 and CR4 are used to prevent excessive voltage from appearing across the gate-to-cathode terminals of the controlled switch, and CR5 is used to prevent transistor action of the controlled switch when positive grid voltage and negative anode potential occur at the same time.

AC CONTROL

The four-layer diode provides an efficient technique for the control of an SCR that is used in turn to control AC power. As shown, a full-wave bridge consisting of diodes D1 through D4 is in series with the load; an SCR (D7) is placed across the center terminals of the bridge so that when the SCR is fired, current will flow through the bridge, the SCR, and the load. The power delivered to the load is controlled by the phase angle at which the SCR fires.

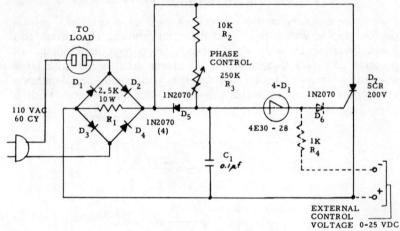

Courtesy Shockley Transistor, Unit Clevite Transistor.
AC control circuit.

A simple RC network and a four-layer diode comprise the firing circuit. At the beginning of each cycle, C1 charges through R2 and R3. The charging rate is controlled by the setting of R3. When the voltage across C1 becomes equal to the switching voltage of the four-layer diode (4-D1), it fires, discharging C1 through the SCR gate and turning on the SCR. At the end of the half cycle, the voltage across the SCR drops to zero, turning off the SCR until it is fired again during the next half-cycle.

Suppose that R3 is at its maximum-resistance position; the time required to charge C1 to the switching voltage of D1 is greater than the period of one-half cycle; therefore, the SCR does not conduct. However, a discharge path must be provided to discharge C1 at the end of each half-cycle to prevent charge build-up on the subsequent half-cycle. This discharge path is through D5 and R1.

If it is desired, the negative bias through R4 can control the firing. D6 prevents breakdown of the SCR in the reverse direction.

CONTROLLED-RECTIFIER MOTOR-SPEED CONTROL

This circuit allows the controlled rectifier to be used to regulate the speed of small universal motors. Motors of this type are used for fans, food mixers and blenders, sewing machines, and various types of hand tools, including drills and saws.

There is no rewiring necessary, since the circuit can be plugged directly into a 117-volt line, and the appliance or tool can be plugged directly into the circuit.

As shown in the circuit diagram, the counter emf of the motor is used as a feedback signal so that it is possible to maintain an effectively constant speed, in spite of the variations in torque. The

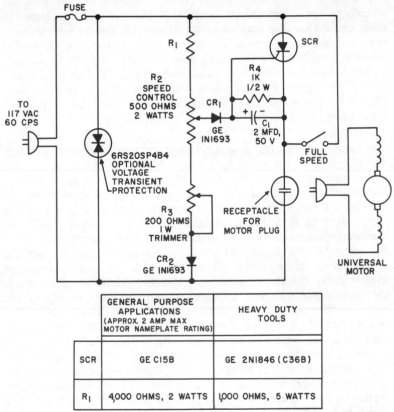

	GENERAL PURPOSE APPLICATIONS (APPROX. 2 AMP MAX MOTOR NAMEPLATE RATING)	HEAVY DUTY TOOLS
SCR	GE C15B	GE 2N1846 (C36B)
R₁	4,000 OHMS, 2 WATTS	1,000 OHMS, 5 WATTS

Courtesy General Electric Co.

Motor-speed control circuit

speed control is R2. When the supply voltage goes positive, a portion of this sine wave is taken off across the control and compared with the counter emf of the motor. When this voltage becomes higher than the armature voltage, current flows through the diode (CR1) and triggers the controlled rectifier. In this way the rest of the positive cycle becomes the supply voltage to the motor.

The speed of the motor tends to decrease as the load is applied to the motor, and this tends to decrease the counter emf. Because of this, the voltage taken from the speed control causes a current flow into the gate of the controlled rectifier somewhat earlier in the cycle; hence, an additional voltage is applied to the armature. This compensates for the increased load and tends to maintain the preset speed. It is possible to obtain about a 3 to 1 speed range with this circuit. It is also possible to close the switch to allow the full speed of the motor at any time.

For most applications, the controlled rectifier can be attached directly to the metal chassis, using the standard mica insulator. In some cases when the duty cycle would cause a greater heat dissipation, it is necessary to provide a separate heat sink for the controlled rectifier. Rectifier CR1 prevents excessive reverse voltage to the gate electrode of the rectifier. CR2 is used to prevent the induced current due to the field of the motor from interfering with the circuit operation. R4 and C1 are used to improve the circuit stability. R3 is a preset control to prevent hunting of the motor.

PHASE-CONTROLLED, SINGLE-PHASE-OUTPUT POWER SUPPLY

A circuit for the control of AC voltage is shown; this design permits the use of controlled rectifiers SCR1 and SCR2 as required by the current. In operation unijunction transistor Q1 is tied across the supply line using a bridge rectifier, CR1 through CR4, and this arrangement allows Q1 to be triggered on both alternations of the incoming AC. As shown, the manual control is resistor R2, and the time constant of the circuit composed of R2, R3, and C1 produces a time delay for the unijunction transistor. After this time delay, the unijunction transistor produces a pulse to the primary of the pulse transformer (T2). This pulse transformer couples the pulses to the gates of the controlled rectifiers SCR3 and SCR4. The rectifier that has a positive anode voltage then fires. This conduction in turn triggers one of the two main controlled rectifiers (SCR1 and SCR2). The alternating-current supply for the two smaller controlled rectifiers (SCR3 and SCR4) is obtained from the filament-type transformer (T1). Breakdown diodes CR5 and CR6, together with resistors R5 and R6, prevent excessive drive to the larger controlled rectifiers. There is a resistor-capacitor combination in series with

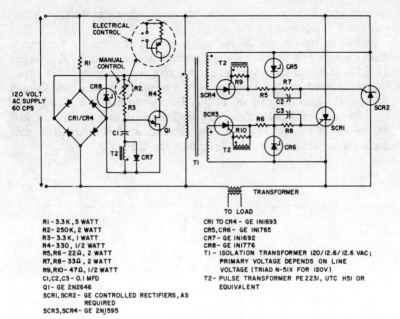

Courtesy General Electric Co.

Phase-controlled power supply circuit.

R1 - 3.3 K , 5 WATT
R2 - 250K, 2 WATT
R3 - 3.3 K, I WATT
R4 - 330, 1/2 WATT
R5, R6 - 22 Ω , 2 WATT
R7, R8 - 33 Ω , 2 WATT
R9, R10 - 47 Ω , 1/2 WATT
C1, C2, C3 - 0.1 MFD
Q1 - GE 2N2646
SCR1, SCR2 - GE CONTROLLED RECTIFIERS, AS
      REQUIRED
SCR3, SCR4 - GE 2N1595

CR1 TO CR4 - GE 1N1693
CR5, CR6 - GE 1N1765
CR7 - GE 1N1692
CR8 - GE 1N1776
T1 - ISOLATION TRANSFORMER 120/12.6/12.6 VAC;
     PRIMARY VOLTAGE DEPENDS ON LINE
     VOLTAGE (TRIAD N-51X FOR 120V)
T2 - PULSE TRANSFORMER PE 2231, UTC H51 OR
     EQUIVALENT

each gate of the main controlled rectifiers (R7 and C2 in shunt and R8 and C3 in shunt). These are used to limit the gate dissipation, although allowing a high gate pulse to trigger the main rectifier. It is also possible, if desired, to use a transistor circuit rather than R2 as the control.

CHANGEOVER SWITCH

The changeover switch is a circuit employing controlled rectifiers to switch one circuit off at the same time another circuit is switched on. In this circuit only one TCR can conduct at a time. In circuit A, when switch S1 is depressed, controlled rectifier TCR1 is biased into conduction. When TCR1 begins to conduct, its anode voltage falls. This voltage change causes a current to flow through the 0.2 mfd capacitor to the anode of TCR2, which in turn brings the anode current of TCR2 below the holding current for a few microseconds. Therefore, TCR2 is switched off at the same time that TCR1 is switched on. If controlled rectifier TCR2 was not conducting when TCR1 started to conduct, TCR2 will remain off. When switch S2 is depressed, controlled rectifier TCR2 is biased into conduction, and TCR1 is cut off. This circuit will operate successfully from –65°C to +125°C with a load current that may vary between the holding current and 200 ma. For loads drawing higher currents, a higher value of C is necessary.

Switching on the anode voltage in circuit B causes a current to flow through C2, which is large enough to turn on TCR1. When TCR1 is switched on, a voltage drop across R3 of about 1 volt exists. Trigger current, caused by pressing the pushbutton, can flow through R5 and D3 into the gate of TCR2. But it can not flow through D1 into the gate of TCR1, since D4 is connected to ground potential. Therefore TCR2 switches on. The operation of the circuit is then the same as that previously described for Circuit A.

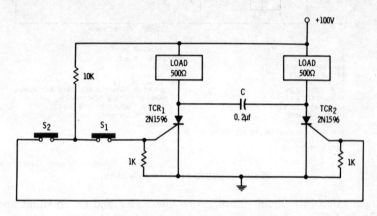

(A) Circuit with two push buttons.

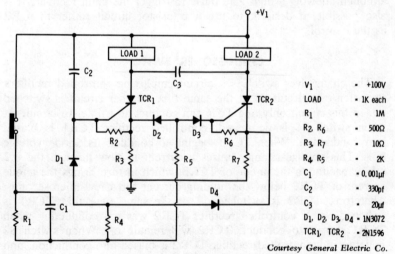

(B) Circuit with one push button.
Changeover switch.

Courtesy General Electric Co.

20

SIMPLE MOTOR CONTROL

The simple motor control is a motor-speed regulator requiring only seven components. This circuit allows a variation in the phase angle of a load current up to 600 ma from 60° to 180° over an ambient temperature range of −65°C to +72°C. AC phase-control circuits using controlled rectifiers can be built in an extremely small space and have a very high efficiency.

When power is applied to the circuit, a small amount of current flows through the motor, resistor R1, and diode D2 during the

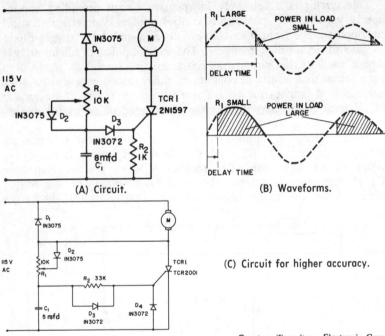

(A) Circuit.

(B) Waveforms.

(C) Circuit for higher accuracy.

Courtesy Transitron Electronic Corp.

Motor control.

positive half-cycle, thus charging capacitor C1. The voltage at the gate of TCR1 reaches the height necessary to trigger the TCR at some time during the positive half-cycle, depending on the value of R1 and the voltage across C1. If R1 is set for maximum resistance (10 kΩ), the delay time will be relatively long, and the power into the motor will be relatively small. If R1 is set for minimum resistance (0Ω), the controlled rectifier will fire immediately after the positive half-cycle begins. Therefore the setting of resistor R1 determines the amount of power to be used by the motor and, consequently, the speed at which the motor will operate. The motor control unit is therefore a delay circuit, the delay time determining the amount of power used by the motor. Since the controlled rectifier has a comparatively small saturation voltage in the On state and absorbs a very small amount of power in the Off state, the efficiency of this circuit is more than 98%. Fig. B shows the waveforms; Fig. C shows a circuit of higher accuracy.

AC PHASE CONTROL 1 USING PNPN TRIGGER DIODES AND CONTROLLED RECTIFIERS

This circuit is a relatively inexpensive circuit providing continuously variable AC phase-shift control with a symmetrical control overload voltage from 0 to 100%. It uses a multilayer trigger diode to gate the controlled rectifiers. The PNPN diffused silicon trigger device used in this circuit has characteristics similar to those of a neon lamp; that is, it will conduct in either direction when the voltage across it reaches the breakdown voltage. It is this characteristic of bilateral conduction that makes the trigger diode useful in this circuit.

When voltage is applied to the circuit, capacitor C1 charges through resistors R1, R2, and R3. During the positive half-cycle, when the anode of controlled rectifier SCR1 is positive, capacitor C1 charges until it reaches the breakdown voltage of the trigger diode. When the trigger diode conducts, capacitor C1 discharges

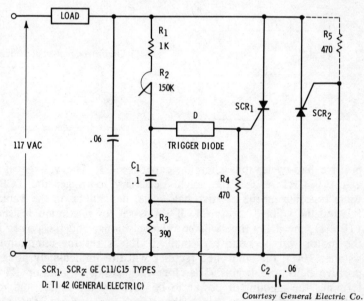

Courtesy General Electric Co.

Circuit of AC phase control 1.

through the trigger diode and resistors R3 and R4. The resulting bias at the gate of SCR1 switches SCR1 on, and current passes through the load for the remainder of that half-cycle. At the end of the positive half-cycle, the anode voltage on SCR1 goes negative and it switches off again. During the negative half-cycle, when the anode of controlled rectifier SCR2 is positive, capacitor C1 again charges until it reaches the breakdown voltage of the trigger diode. When the trigger diode conducts, capacitor C1 discharges through the trigger diode and resistors R3 and R4. The resulting positive pulse developed across resistor R3 is coupled through capacitor C2 to the gate of controlled rectifier SCR2 and switches SCR2 on. Current now flows through the load for the remainder of the half-cycle. Adjustment of variable resistor R2 controls the charge time for C1, thus controlling the triggering time of SCR1 and SCR2. Resistor R5 may be used for additional circuit stability, particularly at higher temperatures with certain low-current SCR's.

AC PHASE CONTROL 2 USING PNPN TRIGGER DIODES AND CONTROLLED RECTIFIERS

When voltage is applied to the circuit, capacitor C1 charges through resistors R1 and R2 and transformer T1. During the positive half-cycle, when the anode of controlled rectifier SCR1 is positive, capacitor C1 charges until it reaches the breakdown voltage of the

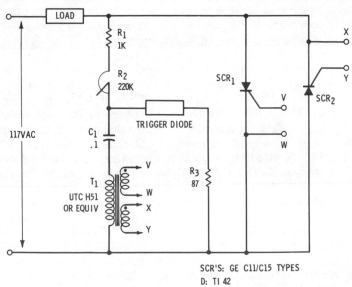

SCR'S: GE C11/C15 TYPES
D: TI 42

Courtesy General Electric Co.

Circuit of AC phase control 2.

23

trigger diode. When the trigger diode conducts, capacitor C1 discharges through the trigger diode, resistor R3, and transformer T1. The resulting pulse is coupled through T1 to the gate of controlled rectifier SCR1. (When wiring transformer T1 into the circuit, the polarity of each winding must be observed.) SCR1 now conducts, passing current through the load for the remainder of the half-cycle.

At the end of the positive half-cycle the anode voltage of SCR1 goes negative and SCR1 switches off again. During the negative half-cycle, when the anode of controlled rectifier SCR2 is positive, capacitor C1 again charges until it reaches the breakdown voltage of the trigger diode. When the trigger diode conducts, capacitor C1 discharges through the trigger diode, resistor R3, and transformer T1. The transformer couples the pulse to the gate of SCR2, which now conducts, passing current through the load for the remainder of the half-cycle.

At the end of the negative half-cycle the anode voltage on SCR2 goes negative and SCR2 switches off again, completing the cycle. Adjustment of variable resistor R2 controls the charge time for C1, thus controlling the triggering time of SCR1 and SCR2.

60 CPS BURST CONTROL

The 60 cps burst-control circuit uses silicon-controlled rectifiers to produce time-controlled, short-duration AC voltage. In the spot welding of metals and in photography such voltages are often required to drive a welding transformer or to energize lamps. This circuit uses two silicon-controlled rectifiers and associated control circuits to time control the AC load voltages.

When the burst control is in the off condition, switch SW1 is in position 1, and the upper plate of capacitor C2 charges to −20 volts. Transistors Q1 and Q2 now operate as a monostable multivibrator with Q1 in cutoff and Q2 saturated. Resistor R3 in the collector circuit of Q2 has the entire DC input voltage of 20 volts across it. The collector of Q2 is therefore at +20 volts, or ground, and there is no voltage to support oscillations in blocking oscillator Q3. When switch SW1 is placed in position 2, the emitter-base junction of Q1 is forward-biased. This drives Q1 into saturation and reverse-biases Q2 into cutoff through capacitor C1. The time Q2 remains in cutoff is determined by the time constant of resistors R1 and R2 and capacitor C1. When Q2 is cut off, Q3 begins to oscillate at a rate of approximately 10,000 cps. The duration of each pulse from the transformer is about 2 μsec. The oscillator pulses from the secondary windings of the transformer gate both silicon-controlled rectifiers in the forward direction. The controlled rectifiers, which are biased in the forward direction, will conduct until the polarity of the input voltage changes; that is, they conduct until Q2 becomes saturated

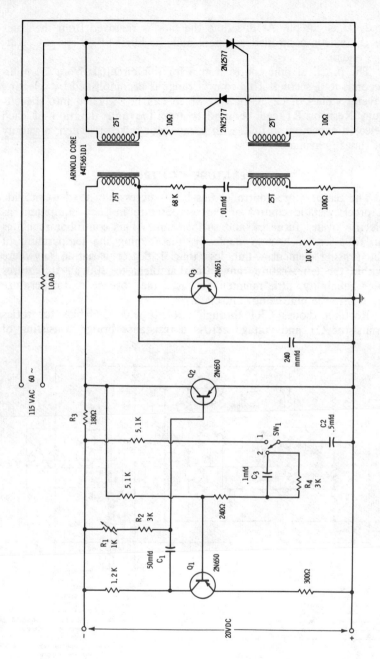

Courtesy Motorola Semiconductor Products, Inc.

Circuit of 60-cps burst control.

25

and Q3 is cut off. At this time the bias is removed from the gates of the silicon-controlled rectifiers and the burst of 60-cps AC voltage ends.

The practical time-control range for this circuit is from 20 milliseconds to 1 second. This control range is accomplished by selecting several values of capacitor C1, which can be switched into the circuit. Resistor R1 can be used to trim the time duration of each selected capacitor so that, with a capacitor selector switch, a variety of times is available.

TEMPERATURE CONTROLLER

The temperature controller has been successfully used to provide a precise, static control of the temperature in such equipment as electric ovens, furnaces, and surface units. This controller regulates up to 4 kw of heaters steplessly, maintaining the temperature at the sensing element within less than 1 degree variation anywhere within the temperature range from ambient to 300°C. It features high reliability, little maintenance, and the absence of temperature cycling in the unit being controlled.

Rectifier diodes CR1 through CR4 provide DC bias for series transistor Q1 and voltage across a resistance bridge consisting of

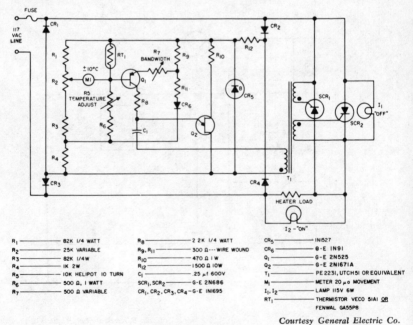

R₁	82K 1/4 WATT	R₈	2 2K 1/4 WATT	CR₅	1N1527
R₂	25K VARIABLE	R₉, R₁₁	300 Ω --- WIRE WOUND	CR₆	G-E 1N91
R₃	82K 1/4W	R₁₀	470 Ω 1 W	Q₁	G-E 2N525
R₄	1K 2W	R₁₂	1500 Ω 10W	Q₂	G-E 2N1671A
R₅	10K HELIPOT 10 TURN	C₁	.25 μf 600V	T₁	PE 2231, UTCH51 OR EQUIVALENT
R₆	500 Ω, 1 WATT	SCR₁, SCR₂	G-E 2N686	M₁	METER 20 μa MOVEMENT
R₇	500 Ω VARIABLE	CR₁, CR₂, CR₃, CR₄	G-E 1N1695	I₁, I₂	LAMP 115V 6W
				RT₁	THERMISTOR VECO 51A1 OR FENWAL GA55P8

Courtesy General Electric Co.

Temperature controller circuit.

resistors R5, R6, R9, R11, thermistor R1, and diode CR6. When the temperature surrounding thermistor RT1 is at the desired level, the resistance of R5 and R6 is equal to the resistance of RT1. Capacitor C1 is charged by series transistor Q1. The base signal on Q1 is developed across the resistance bridge. If the temperature at the thermistor drops below the preset value, the resistance of RT1 increases. The voltage at the base of Q1 decreases, causing more base and collector current to flow. This charges C1 more quickly, and Q2 fires earlier in each cycle. Q2 fires during each positive and negative half-cycle after C1 reaches its triggering voltage.

When Q2 fires, C1 discharges through Q2 and the primary winding of T1, resulting in a positive pulse at the gates of controlled rectifiers SCR1 and SCR2. The phase angle at which SCR1 and SCR2 fire is determined by the discharge time of Q2. If Q2 fires earlier, more power will be applied to the heaters and the temperature will return to the preset value. The reverse action will occur if the temperature rises above the preset value. Meter M1 provides a visual indication of the temperature deviation from the preset value. When the temperature reaches the desired level, R2 is adjusted for a center-scale indication on M1. Lamps I1 and I2 indicate the proportion of the voltage cycle applied to the heating elements. Diode CR6 is inserted in the sensing bridge to temperature-compensate the variation of base-to-emitter voltage of Q1. Thermistor RT1 is designed for temperature control around 150°C. For other temperatures, RT1 should be selected to have approximately the same resistance as R5.

PYROMETER-OPERATED TEMPERATURE CONTROLLER

This circuit uses a commercially available pyrometer delivering about a 0 to 100 volt swing when calling for zero to full output of the furnace heating element. Zener diode CR5 and resistor R1 determine the threshold characteristic of the circuit; R1 also determines the maximum input voltage. Zener diodes CR6 and CR7 and resistor R2 are shown dotted to indicate that they are optional for improving the linearity and the transfer characteristic for large values of the output. Conversely, by omitting this network and making R8 adjustable, the circuit can be linearized over the particular control range of interest.

The charge time for capacitor C1 to reach the triggering level of unijunction transistor Q2 is determined by the values of C1 and R8 and by the output voltage of the pyrometer. When Q2 fires, C1 discharges through T1 and Q1 producing positive pulses at the gates of the controlled rectifiers. These positive pulses trigger the controlled rectifiers into conduction, passing current through the load. The phase angle at which the SCR's are fired is determined

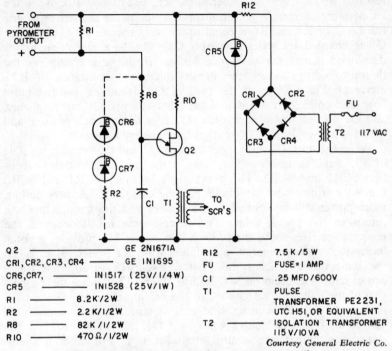

Q2	GE 2N1671A		R12		7.5 K / 5 W
CR1, CR2, CR3, CR4	GE 1N1695		FU		FUSE= 1 AMP
CR6, CR7,	1N1517 (25V/1/4W)		C1		.25 MFD /600V
CR5	1N1528 (25V/1W)		T1		PULSE
R1	8.2K/2W				TRANSFORMER PE2231,
R2	2.2 K/1/2W				UTC H51, OR EQUIVALENT
R8	82 K /1/2W		T2		ISOLATION TRANSFORMER
R10	470 Ω / 1/2W				115 V/10 VA

Courtesy General Electric Co.

Circuit of pyrometer-operated temperature controller.

by the charge time of C1 which is controlled by the DC output of the pyrometer. As the output voltage from the pyrometer increases, the charge time for C1 becomes less, and the SCR's are fired at a smaller phase angle, thus providing more power to the heater load. Conversely, a decreased output voltage from the pyrometer results in less power being applied to the heater load.

SCR CONTROL WITH A UJT-I

The full-wave unijunction transistor (UJT) firing circuit provides full-wave phase control of the load current from 0 to 100%. Adjustment of potentiometer R4 controls the phase angle at which each controlled rectifier (SCR) is fired. This circuit is useful and economical as a lamp-dimming circuit or current control for hobby projects or toys.

During the positive half-cycle, when the voltage at the anode of SCR1 is positive, capacitor C2 charges through resistors R1 and R2 until it reaches the emitter-base 1 breakdown voltage of Q1. Q1 now fires and C2 discharges through R5, producing a positive pulse at the gate of controlled rectifier SCR1. SCR1 now conducts for the

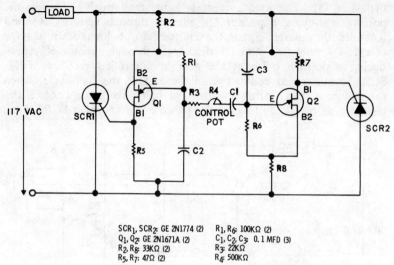

SCR₁, SCR₂: GE 2N1774 (2)   R₁, R₆: 100KΩ (2)
Q₁, Q₂: GE 2N1671A (2)   C₁, C₂, C₃: 0.1 MFD (3)
R₂, R₈: 33KΩ (2)   R₃: 22KΩ
R₅, R₇: 47Ω (2)   R₄: 500KΩ

Courtesy General Electric Co.

Circuit I for control of SCR with UJT.

remainder of the positive half-cycle. At the end of the positive half-cycle, the voltage across SCR1 falls to zero, and it ceases conducting until another pulse is applied to its gate. The charge time of C2 is determined by the RC time constant of C2, R1, and R2 and the time constant of C1 and R3, R4, R6, and R8. (As C2 charges, a portion of the charge is drained off to charge C1.) Therefore, adjustment of control potentiometer R4 controls the phase angle at which SCR1 fires. During the negative half-cycle, when the voltage at the anode of SCR1 is negative, capacitor C3 charges through resistors R6 and R8 until it reaches the emitter-base 1 breakdown voltage of Q2. Q2 fires and C3 discharges through resistor R7, producing a positive pulse at the gate of SCR2. SCR2 now conducts for the remainder of the negative half-cycle. Again the charge time of C3 is controlled by R4 much as the charge time of C2 was controlled. The resulting voltage across the load is symmetrical, since the trigger circuits are identical.

SCR CONTROL WITH A UJT-II

This circuit is an economical phase-control circuit providing a nonsymmetrical phase-control of the load current from 0 to 100%. For half-wave, or low current, phase control, switch S1A is in the right-hand position, placing diode D1 across unijunction transistor (UJT) Q1, and S1B is closed, shorting part of variable resistor R4 During the negative half-cycle, the current flows through D1,

29

bypassing Q1. The load current is kept small by R2. During the positive half-cycle, capacitor C1 charges through resistors R3 and R4 until the charge equals the emitter-base 1 breakdown voltage of Q1. Q1 now fires and C1 discharges through resistor R1, producing a positive pulse at the gate of controlled rectifier SCR1. SCR1 continues to conduct until the end of the half-cycle, when the voltage across it drops to zero. For half-wave phase control, the charge time of C1, and hence the phase angle at which SCR1 fires,

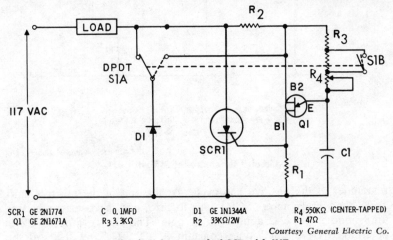

| SCR1 GE 2N1774 | C 0.1MFD | D1 GE 1N1344A | R4 550KΩ (CENTER-TAPPED) |
| Q1 GE 2N1671A | R3 3.3KΩ | R2 33KΩ/2W | R1 47Ω |

Courtesy General Electric Co.

Circuit II for control of SCR with UJT.

is determined by the RC time constant of C1, R3, and potentiometer R4. Therefore, adjustment of R4 will provide phase control during half-wave phase control.

For full-wave phase control, switch S1A is placed in the left-hand position, connecting D1 in series with the load; S1B is open, placing the other half of R4 in series with C1. During the negative half-cycle, the current flows through the load and D1. During the positive half-cycle, capacitor C1 again charges through R3 and R4 (including the top half of R4) until the charge equals the emitter-base 1 breakdown voltage of Q1. Q1 again fires, and a positive pulse triggers SCR1 into conduction as in the case for half-wave phase control. Again, adjustment of R4 controls the charge time of C1, thus controlling the phase angle at which SCR1 fires.

REMOTE POWER CONTROL

This circuit shows the use of DA3F3 transistors in a circuit that can control up to 200 watts of power as indicated. A pair of transistors is used in this remote-control circuit with the line voltage being 117 volts AC.

30

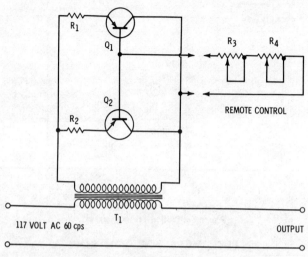

R₁

Q₁

Q₂

R₂

R₃   **R₄**

REMOTE CONTROL

T₁

117 VOLT AC 60 cps

OUTPUT

Parts List

T₁   Filament Power Transformer (Stancor P6461 or equivalent)
Q₁&Q₂ Minneapolis-Honeywell Power Transistor Type DA3F3
R₁&R₂ .1 ohm
R₃   Variable Rheostat 1 Watt 1000 Ohms
R₄   Variable Rheostat 1 Watt 30 Ohms

Courtesy Minneapolis-Honeywell Regulator Co.
Remote power-control circuit.

The remote-control network (R3 and R4) controls the pair of transistors. These transistors in turn control the drop across the transformer which, in effect, varies the output power. This circuit can handle up to 200 watts with a circuit efficiency of more than 90%. This makes the circuit suitable for limiting power used for lamps, soldering irons, or filament heaters. It is possible to mount the control potentiometers at some remote position. The transistors should be mounted on a heat sink for the best power dissipation.

SCR PHASE-CONTROLLED TRIGGER

One of the many variations for the firing of silicon-controlled recifiers is shown in this cicuit. The 1K resistor and 50K potentio-meter are in series with the capacitor across the 117-volt line. When the capacitor reaches a sufficiently high voltage, the neon lamp fires and produces a sharp pulse through the transformer primary. There are two transformer secondaries, one connecting to each of the controlled rectifiers, as shown in the circuit. The rectifiers are con-nected back to back and fired from the control signal created by the current flow through the primary of the transformer.

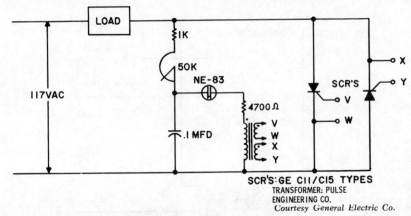

SCR'S: GE C11/C15 TYPES
TRANSFORMER: PULSE
ENGINEERING CO.
Courtesy General Electric Co.

Phase-controlled trigger circuit.

FULL-WAVE SCR CONTROL

Full-wave operation of a silicon-controlled rectifier is shown. The slave RC circuit supplies the gate current for SCR2. The value of resistor R1 in the slave circuit is that which is required to hold SCR2 off.

Capacitor C1 together with the resistor provide the required time constant. When the line voltage goes in a positive direction for the anode of the SCR2, capacitor C2 charges toward the positive-going line from a negative original voltage. The size of this negative voltage depends on the time constant of the RC network (R1 and C1) and the conduction interval of SCR1.

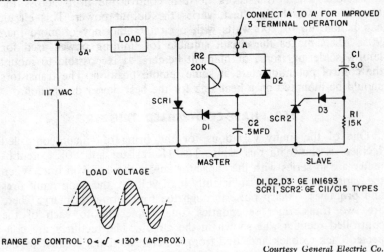

RANGE OF CONTROL: $0 < \alpha < 130°$ (APPROX.)

D1, D2, D3: GE 1N1693
SCR1, SCR2: GE C11/C15 TYPES

Courtesy General Electric Co.

Full-wave SCR control circuit.

Suppose that SCR1 did not conduct during any part of the half cycle that is negative for SCR2; then the voltage across C1 is a maximum. When the anode of SCR2 is positive, capacitor C1 must charge toward the positive-going line voltage from a maximum negative value, so that there is a delay angle large enough to hold SCR2 off.

If SCR1 conducts early in its positive half-cycle, capacitor C2 charges from a very small initial voltage, causing SCR2 to enter conduction early in its half-cycle.

TIMERS

MULTIVIBRATOR TIMER

This circuit demonstrates a one-shot multivibrator used as a timer. Its purpose is to close the relay for a selected period of time after the closing of a switch. The contacts of the relay in this particular circuit can handle 2 amperes at 115 volts, although it is possible to use this relay to drive another relay if larger amounts of power are to be handled.

There are two transistors shown in the circuit; Q1 is normally conducting, while Q2 is normally off. After switch S1 is closed, the base of transistor Q1 is essentially brought to ground potential since capacitor C2 has no charge. This causes the collector current of Q1 to be transferred to the base of Q2, which then conducts, closing the relay. The base of Q1 then becomes about 6 volts negative because of the initial voltage across capacitor C1. Now Q2 is conducting, and Q1 is not conducting.

While Q2 is on, capacitor C1 is discharging toward +6 volts through R2 and R3. However, when the base voltage of Q1 has become slightly positive, this transistor conducts and turns off the other transistor so that the relay is opened, completing the cycle. Capacitor C1, R2, and R3 control the operating time. Note that capacitor C1 is an electrolytic capacitor. It is possible to switch various values of C1 into the circuit if desired. Resistor R4 protects transistor Q1, diode CR1 is a clamp across the relay, and resistor R5 keeps capacitor C2 discharged until switch S1 is closed. Battery B1 keeps Q2 off when Q1 is conducting.

Since battery B1 draws a very small current, it need not be disconnected from the circuit. Consequently switch section S2B may be omitted from the circuit if desired.

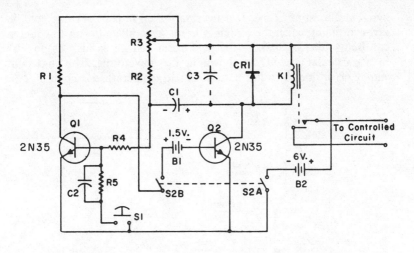

CR1 - 1N34 Diode.
K1 - 6V., 300Ω or greater Relay (such as Potter
    & Brumfield RS5D).
Q1, Q2 - Sylvania 2N35 Transistor.
R1 - 3.3K, 1/2w. Resistor.
R2 - 4.7K, 1/2w. Resistor.
R3 - 25K Potentiometer.
R4 - 150Ω, 1/2w. Resistor.
R5 - 1 meg. 1/2w. Resistor.
S1 - Switch (any sort of normally open push
    button, or may be toggle switch left normal-
    ly open and closed momentarily to initiate
    relay closure).
S2 - D.P.S.T. Switch.

B1 - 1 to 1.5V. Battery (such as penlite cell or
    small mercury cell).
B2 - 6V. Battery (such as lantern type or "A"
    type).
C1 - Electrolytic Capacitor, 6V. or greater.

	Relay ON Time
C1 Value	(controlled by R3 setting)
2000 Mfd.	1 min. to 10 sec.
1000 Mfd.	60 sec. to 5 sec.
200 Mfd.	6 sec. to 1 sec.
100 Mfd.	3 sec. to .5 sec.

C2 - .05 to 1 Paper Capacitor.
C3 - .05 Paper Capacitor.

Courtesy Sylvania Electric Products, Inc.

Multivibrator timer circuit.

TIMING CIRCUIT

A relatively simple but efficient timing circuit is shown in the
figure. It is capable of giving a time delay from 0.01 second up to
about 40 seconds and can be operated directly from 117-volt AC
input. To start the circuit, switch S1 is moved to the Reset position.
Capacitor C1 then charges up to the peak value of the line voltage
through CR2 and R1. To begin the actual timing, switch S1 is thrown
to the opposite, or Time, position. When this happens, capacitor C1
discharges at a rate determined by C1 and resistors R2 and R3.

Resistor R3 controls the stabilizing bias current through CR3, and
this controls the negative gate voltage on the semiconductor-con-
trolled rectifier. When the voltage on capacitor C1 reaches the
proper magnitude, the SCR turns on and ends the timing cycle. The
stabilizing bias for the SCR decreases as capacitor C1 discharges
so that there is a region near the end of the capacitor discharge
where the SCR is not completely stable and, therefore, can be trig

gered at almost any time. It is necessary then to consider this possible error in timing when the circuit is used. Any difficulties in this region can be avoided by making the peak reset voltage as high as possible in a particular circuit, as shown in the waveforms. The maximum timing error due to circuit variations and temperature is about 1.2%.

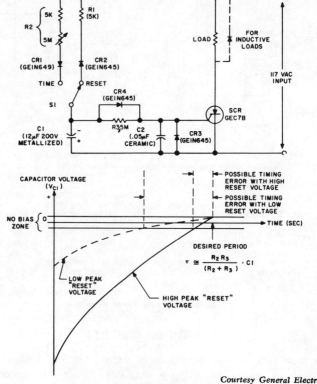

Courtesy General Electric Co.

Timing circuit.

LONG TIME-DELAY CIRCUIT

A long time delay can be obtained with the four-layer diode in the circuit as shown. To obtain a time delay of a minute or so usually requires a large value of capacitance. However, high-quality, low-leakage capacitors are usually expensive. In this circuit resistor R1 is greater than 1 or 2 megohms to permit the use of a smaller timing capacitor for a long time delay. This long time-delay circuit requires only that resistor R1 be lower than the leakage resistances of capacitor C1 and diode CR1.

This circuit has a pulse generator (4D-1) that drives a diode gate

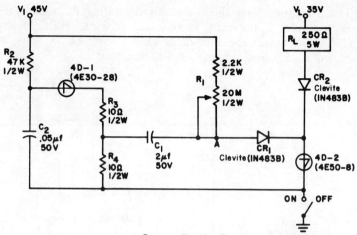

Courtesy Shockley Transistor, Unit Clevite Transistor.
Long time-delay circuit.

to an RC timing network. When the off-on switch is closed, capacitor C1 begins to charge through R1 and the impedance of the pulse generator toward voltage V1. After the predetermined time the voltage at point A exceeds voltage V_L, and diode gate CR1 opens. This voltage at point A is an exponential charging voltage plus a series of short duration pulses coming from the pulse generator. When the diode gate opens, a pulse from the generator triggers four-layer diode 4D-2; it will remain on in a very low-resistance mode of operation and carry the load current until the off-on switch is again opened. The circuit switches 35 volts across a 250-ohm load after a 60-second delay.

SHORT TIME-DELAY CIRCUIT

The figure shows a circuit using the four-layer diode in a time-delay circuit of moderate duration. At the end of a specific delay time the supply voltage is switched across the load. In this circuit the four-layer diode is used with a switching voltage which is greater than the supply voltage. When the on-off switch is closed, conventional diode CR1 is back-biased, even though there is a small amount of initial current flow through the load.

Capacitor C1 charges toward voltage V1 with a time constant determined by C1 and resistors R1 and R2. However, when switching voltage Vs is reached, the four-layer diode switches on, provided resistor R1 is of a value that passes the switching current. The four-layer diode switches to the low-resistance state, and capacitor C1 discharges into it through R2.

Thus, the four layer diode remains on during the time that the holding current is provided; in this way power is switched to the load. In this circuit the time-delay circuit switches 25 volts, after a delay of 0.25 seconds, across a 2,500-ohm load.

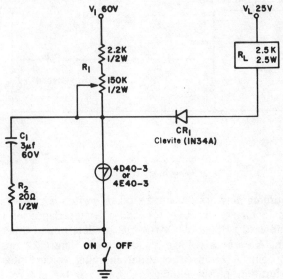

Courtesy Shockley Transistor, Unit Clevite Transistor.
Short time-delay circuit.

INTERVAL TIMER

The interval timer is a novel device that provides an automatic timing signal which may be used for timing moves in a chess game, or any similar type game where time intervals are important. The interval timer features a variable-frequency audio tone, a variable-interval time from 7 to 25 seconds, and a volume control. The interval timer consists of four basic circuits: time-interval generator Q1 and Q2; audio oscillator Q3 and Q4; gate Q8; and audio amplifier Q5, Q6, and Q7.

Transistors Q1 and Q2 form a free-running multivibrator which generates the time-interval gate. Resistors R1 and R7 are collector load resistors. When Q1 conducts, Q2 is cut off and a large bias current for gate transistor Q8 flows through resistors R13, R14, and R15, effectively removing bias from audio amplifiers Q5, Q6, and Q7. Therefore no audio output is heard. When Q1 is cut off, the bias for Q8 is decreased and Q8 is cut off. This provides bias voltage for the audio amplifier section, and the audio tone is heard as a beep. The setting of potentiometer R3 determines the time interval from

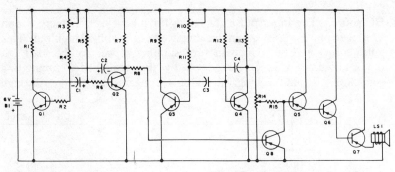

B1 — 6-volt battery
C1 — 10 mfd, electrolytic, 15-volt
C2 — 80 mfd, electrolytic, 15-volt
C3, C4 — 0.0047 mfd disc ceramic or paper
LS1 — 4 to 8-ohm loudspeaker
Q1, Q2, Q3, Q4, Q5, Q6, Q8 — Sylvania
   2N1265 transistor

Q7 — Sylvania 2N255 power transistor
R1, R7, R9, R13 — 20 k, ½ w
R2, R6 — 4.7 k, ½ w
R3, R10, R14 — 250 k potentiometer, ½ w
R4 — 68 k, ½ w
R5 — 620 k, ½ w
R8, R11, R12 — 100 k, ½ w
R15 — 47 k, ½ w

Courtesy Sylvania Electric Products, Inc.

Interval-timer circuit.

the beginning of one beep to the beginning of the next. The time interval is adjustable from 7 to 25 seconds. Transistor Q1 conducts for a much longer interval than does Q2. Resistors R2, R3, and R4 are the base bias resistors for Q1 and resistors R5 and R6 are the base bias resistors for Q2.

The audio oscillator, composed of Q3 and Q4, operates in a similar manner to the time-interval generator, but at a much faster rate. When Q3 conducts, Q4 is cut off and vice versa.

The multivibrator action of Q3 and Q4 generates an audio signal which can be varied from 400 cycles per second to 1.5 kilocycles per second by adjusting potentiometer R10. The audio signal from the collector of Q4 is applied through resistors R14 and R15 to the base of audio amplifier Q5. When gating transistor Q8 is conducting, the three-stage, direct-coupled, audio-amplifier section, composed of transistors Q5, Q6, and Q7, is cut off, and no audio is passed to the speaker. When gating transistor Q8 is cut off, Q5, Q6, and Q7 are biased into conduction, and the audio signal from the collector of Q4 is amplified by the audio amplifier section. The amplified audio signal from the emitter of Q7 is applied to speaker LS1. By connecting the audio amplifiers as emitter followers, high input impedance and low output impedance are obtained.

TIMER WITH HIGH-LEVEL OUTPUT

This circuit, which uses the controlled switch (high-sensitivity SCR), provides a 1 ampere current for 1 second, using a 28-volt

DC source. The input pulse starts the timing cycle; a 5 microsecond or longer pulse with a minimum amplitude of 1 volt is required. This pulse turns on CS1, which in turn supplies power to the load. At the same time, CS2 is turned off by the action of commutating capacitor C1, and timing capacitor C2 begins to charge through

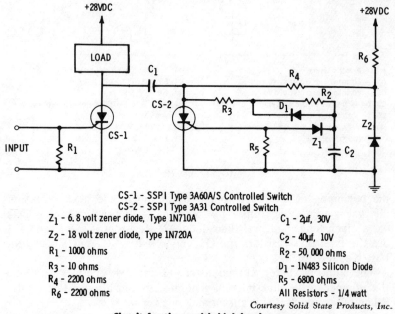

CS-1 - SSPI Type 3A60A/S Controlled Switch
CS-2 - SSPI Type 3A31 Controlled Switch

Z_1 - 6.8 volt zener diode, Type 1N710A
Z_2 - 18 volt zener diode, Type 1N720A
R_1 - 1000 ohms
R_3 - 10 ohms
R_4 - 2200 ohms
R_6 - 2200 ohms

C_1 - 2μf, 30V
C_2 - 40μf, 10V
R_2 - 50,000 ohms
D_1 - 1N483 Silicon Diode
R_5 - 6800 ohms
All Resistors - 1/4 watt

Courtesy Solid State Products, Inc.

Circuit for timer with high-level output.

R2, R3, and R4. Zener diode Z2 is used to establish a fixed charging-voltage source and minimizes timing error due to variations in the source voltage. When the charge on C2 reaches approximately 7.5 volts, zener diode Z1 conducts sufficiently to cause CS2 to fire. This occurs 1 second after the initiating pulse and turns off CS1 due to the action of commutating capacitor C1; power is thus removed from the load. Diode D1 and R3 discharge C2 rapidly so that the total recycle time is less than 1 millisecond.

ACCURATE TIME-DELAY CIRCUIT

The accurate time-delay circuit uses a zener diode and a controlled rectifier to provide a delay of from 0 to 60 seconds. The main advantage in using controlled rectifiers lies in the fact that with one single stage a relatively high power can be switched on. With a -6 volt bias present at V2 and a 50-volt anode voltage applied to the circuit, a 10-second delay can be achieved with a 100-ma load current with the parts values given in the parts list. The accurate time-delay circuit gives an accuracy of ±15% for the whole production spread and ±10% over a temperature range from −65°C to +75°C ambient. The maximum time delay possible from this circuit is well over 60 seconds.

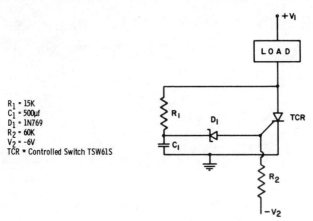

R_1 = 15K
C_1 = 500µf
D_1 = 1N769
R_2 = 60K
V_2 = -6V
TCR = Controlled Switch TSW61S

Courtesy Transitron Electronic Corp.

Accurate time-delay circuit.

When the positive voltage is applied to V1, capacitor C1 starts charging through resistor R1. When C1 reaches the breakdown voltage of zener diode D1, current flows into the gate of the TCR and switches the TCR on. Bias voltage V2 provides a slightly higher accuracy and delay time than can be achieved with a resistance bias.

EXTERNALLY TRIGGERED TIME-DELAY CIRCUIT

The externally triggered time-delay circuit uses a zener diode, a controlled rectifier, and an RC network to produce the time delay and a controlled rectifier to trigger the delay network. By using controlled rectifiers for the delay circuit, only one stage is needed for relatively high power switching. When voltage is applied at V1, the delay circuit is not energized due to the high impedance of controlled rectifier TCR2. When a positive trigger or pulse is applied to the gate of TCR2, TCR2 starts conducting. Immediately after the start pulse, V1 appears across TCR1 and the delay mechanism begins to operate. Resistor R4 provides a path for a current which has to be higher than the holding current of TCR2 in order to have TCR2 remain on after it is switched on. Capacitor C1 now starts charging through resistor R1. When C1 reaches the breakdown volt-

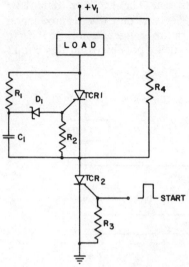

For V_1 = 50V, TCR2 is a 2N1595, R_3 = 1K, and R_4 = 5K

Courtesy Transitron Electronic Corp.

Externally triggered time-delay circuit.

age of zener diode D1, current flows into the gate of TCR1 and switches TCR1 on. The delay time of this circuit is almost linearly dependent on voltage V1 and the values of resistor R1 and capacitor C1.

The externally triggered time-delay circuit is ideally suited for remote starting of appliances, remote relay operation, and so on.

AC TIME-DELAY CIRCUIT

The AC time-delay circuit provides a delay time of about 30 seconds. The accuracy of this circuit is $\pm 10\%$ from -65 to $+75°C$. The main advantage in using controlled rectifiers lies in the fact that with one single stage a relatively high power can be used. The basic difference between the AC time-delay circuit and a DC time-delay circuit is the addition of diode D1.

When the 115-volt AC line voltage is applied to the delay circuit, controlled rectifier TCR1 is off, providing an extremely high impedance in series with the load. This high impedance blocks any current from the load. Diode D1 rectifies the applied AC voltage, providing a DC current through D1, resistor R1, and capacitor C1. Capacitor C1 starts charging through resistor R1. When C1 reaches the breakdown voltage of zener diode D2, a bias current is applied to the gate of controlled rectifier TCR1, switching it on. When TCR1 is on, it offers a very low impedance to the voltage, and the

42

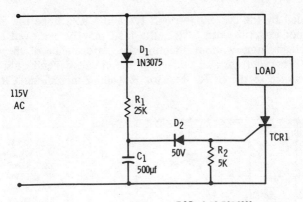

TCR-1 IS TCR2001

Courtesy Transitron Electronic Corp.

AC time-delay circuit.

line voltage now appears across the load. A positive voltage stays on the gate of TCR1 after the delay time has elapsed and the TCR has switched on. This is necessary because the controlled rectifier switches off in the negative half-cycle and will not switch on again without a constant positive signal at the gate. Resistor R2 is the bias-developing resistor for the gate bias on TCR1.

PRECISION DC TIME DELAY

Time-delay circuits are frequently used in industrial controls and aircraft and missile systems to apply or remove power from a load a predetermined time after an initiating signal is applied. Cascaded time-delay circuits can be used to sequentially perform a series of timed operations. This circuit illustrates an extremely simple yet accurate and versatile solid-state, time-delay circuit.

When power is applied to the time-delay circuit, controlled rectifier SCR1 is off and no current can pass to the load. Timing is initiated either by applying supply voltage to the circuit or by opening a shorting contact across C1. Capacitor C1 is now charged through resistors R1 and R2 until the charge equals the emitter-base 1 breakdown voltage of unijunction transistor Q1. At this time Q1 fires and C1 discharges through R4 and Q1, producing a positive pulse at the gate of controlled rectifier SCR1. The time required for the charge on C1 to reach the emitter-base 1 breakdown voltage of Q1 is determined by the RC time constant of C1 and resistors R1 and R2; adjustment of R2 varies the delay time. The positive pulse at the gate of SCR1 switches it on, and current is allowed to pass through the load. When SCR1 fires, the voltage across Q1 falls to less than 2 volts due to the clamping action of CR2. Holding current for SCR1

43

is provided by the current through R5 and CR2. Since the external load is not in series with SCR1, the load may be removed or connected at any time without affecting the performance of the circuit. The operating current and voltage of the circuit depend only on the proper choice of the SCR. Resistor R5 and Zener diode CR1 pro-

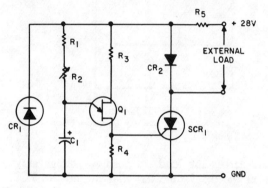

R1 - 2.2K, 1/2 WATT
R2 - IK TO 500K LINEAR POT.
R3 - 150 Ω, 1/2 WATT
R4 - 27, Ω, 1/2 WATT
R5 - 560 Ω, 2 WATT
C1 - 0.2 TO 100 mfd, 15V
SCR1 - G-E 2N1930 OR 2N1771
CR1 - 18V, 10%, 1 WATT ZENER
CR2 - G-E 1N1692
Q1 - G-E 2N1671B

Courtesy General Electric Co.

DC-time-delay circuit.

vide a stable voltage supply for unijunction transistor Q1. The time delay of the circuit can be set to any desired value by appropriate choice of R1, R2, and C1. The upper limit of time delay that can be achieved depends on the required accuracy, the peak point current of the UJT, the maximum ambient temperature, and the leakage current of the capacitor and UJT at the maximum ambient temperature.

VARIABLE TIME CONTROL

This circuit illustrates a time-delay circuit using a relay output with a push-button initiation of the timing sequence. In the quiescent state, controlled rectifier SCR_1 is on, and relay S_1 is energized. Contact S1A is closed, shorting out the timing capacitor C3. To initiate the timing cycle, push-button switch SW2 is momentarily closed, shorting SCR1 through contact S1B and causing SCR1 to turn off. When SW2 is released, S1 is de-energized, and the timing sequence begins.

The 115-volt AC source is coupled through transformer T1 and rectified by full-wave bridge-rectifier diodes CR1 through CR4. Capacitor C1 filters the rectifier output. Zener diode CR7, connected across unijunction transistor Q1, maintains a stable voltage supply for Q1. Capacitor C3 now charges through resistors R5, R7 or R8, and R10 as selected by time-range switch SW1. The settings of SW1, R5, and R10 determine the charge time for C3 to reach the emitter-

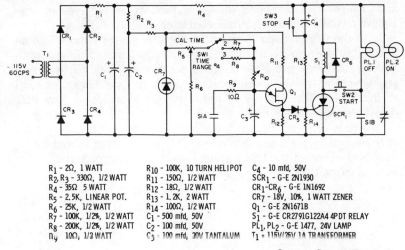

R_1 - 2Ω, 1 WATT	R_{10} - 100K, 10 TURN HELIPOT	C_4 - 10 mfd, 50V
R_2, R_3 - 330Ω, 1/2 WATT	R_{11} - 150Ω, 1/2 WATT	SCR_1 - G-E 2N1930
R_4 - 35Ω 5 WATT	R_{12} - 18Ω, 1/2 WATT	CR_1-CR_6 - G-E 1N1692
R_5 - 2.5K, LINEAR POT.	R_{13} - 1.2K, 2 WATT	CR_7 - 18V, 10%, 1 WATT ZENER
R_6 - 25K, 1/2 WATT	R_{14} - 100Ω, 1/2 WATT	Q_1 - G-E 2N1671B
R_7 - 100K, 1/2%, 1/2 WATT	C_1 - 500 mfd, 50V	S_1 - G-E CR2791G122A4 4PDT RELAY
R_8 - 200K, 1/2%, 1/2 WATT	C_2 - 100 mfd, 50V	PL_1, PL_2 - G-E 1477, 24V LAMP
R_9 - 10Ω, 1/2 WATT	C_3 - 100 mfd, 20V TANTALUM	T_1 - 115V/25V 1A TRANSFORMER

Courtesy General Electric Co.

Variable time-control circuit.

base 1 breakdown voltage of Q1. When C3 is charged to this point, it discharges through R12 and Q1, producing a positive pulse at the gate of SCR1. SCR1 is now switched on again, energizing relay S1. The timing interval is determined by the setting of precision ten-turn *Helipot* R10, which may be set for from 0.25 to 10.25 seconds in increments of 0.01 second. The initial setting of 0.25 seconds takes the added series resistance of time-calibration potentiometer R5 into account. Additional series resistance of 100K and 200K may be added by SW1 to extend the time range by 10 seconds and 20 seconds. A fourth position of SW1 open-circuits the timing resistors and permits unrestricted on-off control of the circuit.

SCR TIME-DELAY CIRCUITS

Controlled rectifiers offer various possibilities of time-delay circuits where, after a specified time, the gate trigger turns the controlled rectifier on, enabling the rectifier to carry large amounts of current.

Circuit A shows the simplest type of circuit that can be used. There are two resistors, one zener diode and a capacitor. When a DC voltage of about 100 to 200 volts is applied, the capacitor becomes charged through its series resistance and the load. When the voltage across this capacitor reaches the breakdown voltage of the zener diode, there will be current flow into the gate of the controlled rectifier. This turns the controlled rectifier on and allows power to pass through the load. This circuit can be modified by different values

45

and changes in the applied voltage, depending on the type of controlled rectifier and its electrical characteristics.

With the values given in circuit A there is a time delay of about 7 seconds with an accuracy of about $\pm10\%$ with ordinary components at room temperature. It is possible to vary the value of series resistor R1 and capacitor C in order to have larger amounts of time delay. The leakage of this capacitor is critical if long time delays are to be obtained.

The time delay of circuit A is dependent on the applied voltage. It is possible to avoid this dependency by using a second zener diode, as shown in circuit B. Here a second zener diode is connected across R2 and capacitor C.

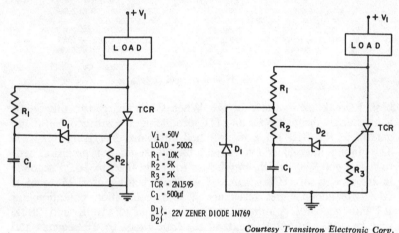

V_1 = 50V
LOAD = 500Ω
R_1 = 10K
R_2 = 5K
R_3 = 5K
TCR = 2N1595
C_1 = 500µf

$\left.\begin{matrix} D_1 \\ D_2 \end{matrix}\right\}$ = 22V ZENER DIODE 1N769

Courtesy Transitron Electronic Corp.

(A) Circuit with delay affected by supply voltage.

(B) Circuit for delay independent of supply voltage.

SCR time-delay circuits.

SECTION 4

INDICATORS

FLAME MONITOR

This illustration shows a cadmium sulphide cell, or light-dependent resistor, in a circuit that can be used for monitoring a flame, as in an oil burner. A photoconductive cell and a trigger tube are used in this circuit. The input voltage, as shown, is 220 volts AC, and there is a voltage divider (R1, R2, and R3) across this AC supply. The photoconductive cell is connected to the tap of resistor R2. Output from this light-dependent resistor is coupled by means of R5 to the trigger tube. When the cell is illuminated, its resistance decreases

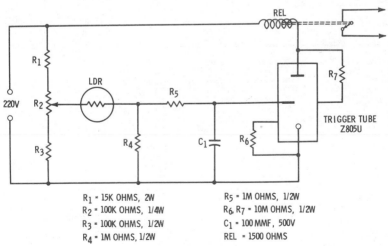

R_1 = 15K OHMS, 2W	R_5 = 1M OHMS, 1/2W
R_2 = 100K OHMS, 1/4W	R_6, R_7 = 10M OHMS, 1/2W
R_3 = 100K OHMS, 1/2W	C_1 = 100 MMF, 500V
R_4 = 1M OHMS, 1/2W	REL = 1500 OHMS

Courtesy Burroughs Corporation of America

Flame-monitor circuit.

so that the voltage input to the trigger tube increases. Above a given level of illumination the voltage on the trigger tube increases beyond the ignition voltage, the trigger tube is fired, and the AC relay is energized. Trigger current is limited by resistor R5, and control R2 is used to set the initial circuit conditions.

In this application the flame is "watched" by the photoconductive cell placed in an air intake duct. If the oil in an oil burner has not been ignited in a certain time after the oil flow is started and the igniter operated, this monitoring system will automatically cut off the oil supply and ring an alarm. If, however, the ignition does take place promptly, the monitoring system will switch off the ignition arrangement.

STROBOSCOPE

This four-transistor stroboscope circuit is used to vary the firing of a neon lamp at a controlled rate. The neon lamp is used for the illumination of a rotating object, such as a fan or motor, to make it appear stationary. If it is properly calibrated, a stroboscope can be used as a tachometer.

The first portion of the circuit, which includes the transistors Q1

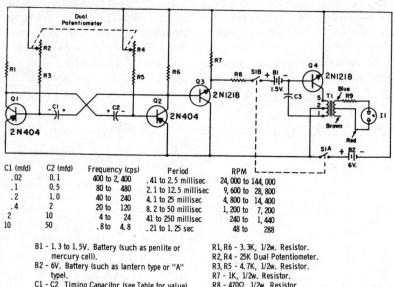

C1 (mfd)	C2 (mfd)	Frequency (cps)	Period	RPM
.02	0.1	400 to 2,400	.41 to 2.5 millisec	24,000 to 144,000
.1	0.5	80 to 480	2.1 to 12.5 millisec	9,600 to 28,800
.2	1.0	40 to 240	4.1 to 25 millisec	4,800 to 14,400
.4	2	20 to 120	8.2 to 50 millisec	1,200 to 7,200
2	10	4 to 24	41 to 250 millisec	240 to 1,440
10	50	.8 to 4.8	.21 to 1.25 sec	48 to 288

B1 - 1.3 to 1.5V. Battery (such as penlite or mercury cell).
B2 - 6V. Battery (such as lantern type or "A" type).
C1 - C2 Timing Capacitor (see Table for value).
C3 - 0.1 Paper Capacitor.
I1 - NE-36 Lamp.
Q1, Q2 - Sylvania 2N404 Transistor.
Q3, Q4 - Sylvania 2N1218 Transistor.

R1, R6 - 3.3K, 1/2w. Resistor.
R2, R4 - 25K Dual Potentiometer.
R3, R5 - 4.7K, 1/2w. Resistor.
R7 - 1K, 1/2w. Resistor.
R8 - 470Ω, 1/2w. Resistor.
R9 - 1.2K, 1/2w. Resistor.
S1 - D.P.S.T. Switch.
T1 - Output Transformer (numbers show connections to be made to secondary terminals) (such as Triad Type S-51X).

Courtesy Sylvania Electric Products, Inc.

Stroboscope circuit.

and Q2, forms a multivibrator that is free-running at the frequency set by the dual potentiometer. The frequency may also be varied by changing the values of the two capacitors (C1 and C2).

In this circuit, when transistor Q2 is conducting, emitter follower Q3 also conducts, causing Q4 to conduct. Transistor Q4 is connected in a blocking-oscillator circuit. Thus, whenever Q2 is on, the blocking oscillator circuit produces a burst of pulses that are stepped up by the transformer to the voltage necessary for the neon lamp. The neon lamp will conduct in both directions because of the overshoot from the transformer secondary.

The table shown with the figure has five columns. The first two are values for capacitors C1 and C2, respectively. The third column is frequency in cycles per second, the fourth column indicates the period, and the final column indicates the revolutions per minute for a rotating object to appear motionless using this circuit.

ALTERNATING LIGHT BLINKER

This circuit shows four transistors used to alternately light two different lamps. A multivibrator is formed by transistors Q1 and Q2, while transistors Q3 and Q4 are power transistors used as emitter followers. In this circuit Q1 conducts with Q3, causing lamp 1 to light; and Q2 conducts with Q4, causing lamp 2 to light. The on time for

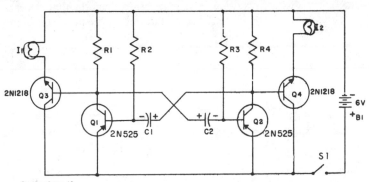

On time Lamp I1
or Off time Lamp I2 = 0.69 R3 C2

On time Lamp I2
or Off time Lamp I1 = 0.69 R2 C1

Time of one cycle = 0.69 (R2C1 + R3C2)
In the above expressions, R's are in ohms, C's are in farads, and time is in seconds.

B1 - 6V. Battery (such as lantern type).
C1, C2 - 100 mfd, 6V. or greater Electrolytic
    Capacitor.
I1, I2 - 6-8V., 0.15 to 0.25 A. Lamp (such as
Nos. 40, 44, 46, 47).

Q1, Q2 - Sylvania 2N525 Transistor.
Q3, Q4 - Sylvania 2N1218 Transistor.
R1, R4 - 1.2K 1/2w. Resistor.
R2, R3 - 5.6K, 1/2w. Resistor.
S1 - S.P.S.T. Switch.

Courtesy of Sylvania Electric Products, Inc.

Alternating-light blinker circuit.

lamp 1 (or the off time for lamp 2) is a function of the value of R3 and C2. The on time of lamp 2 (or the off time of lamp 1) is a function of R2 and C1. The time for a complete cycle depends on all of these values. It is possible to replace resistors R3 or R4 with a 5,000-ohm control in series with a 1,000-ohm resistor. It is also possible to vary the values of capacitors C1 and C2 as desired.

BLINKER LIGHT

This figure shows a simple two-transistor blinker light with both transistors (Q1 and Q2) in a direct-coupled amplifier circuit. The lamp is used as the load in the collector circuit of Q2.

Initially the lamp is off, and control R1 is advanced enough to make Q1 conduct a small amount. Because of this the voltage across the lamp increases, and the base of Q1 becomes more negative because the voltage across the lamp is coupled to Q1 through capacitor C1 and R5. Transistor Q1 conducts more heavily as does Q2 until most of the applied 6 volts in the battery is across the lamp. C1 is charging up so that the current which is applied to the base of Q1 is decreasing. At some point this capacitor becomes charged sufficiently so that Q1 cannot hold Q2 in saturation, and the voltage across the lamp begins to drop. This causes the base current of Q1 to decrease further, resulting in a regenerative action that decreases the voltage across the lamp. This action continues until the lamp is

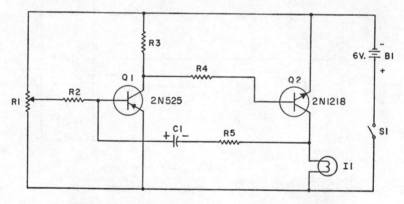

B1 - 6V. Battery (such as lantern type).
C1 - 100 mfd, 6V. or greater Electrolytic Capacitor.
I1 - 6-8V. between .15 and .25 A. Lamp. (such as Nos. 40, 44, 46, 47).
Q1 - Sylvania 2N525 Transistor.
Q2 - Sylvania 2N1218 Transistor.

R1 - 10K, 1/2w. Potentiometer.
R2 - 6.8K, 1/2w. Resistor.
R3 - 1K, 1/2w. Resistor.
R4 - 270Ω, 1/2w. Resistor.
R5 - 1.8K, 1/2w. Resistor.
S1 - S.P.S.T. Switch.

Courtesy Sylvania Electric Products, Inc.
Circuit for blinker light.

off and the base of Q1 is driven positive because of the charge on C1.

At this point both transistors are off, and the charge which was on C1 leaks off through the path R1, R2, R5, and the lamp. The base voltage of Q1 increases to the level determined by the control setting, and, when the base of Q1 becomes slightly negative, the cycle repeats.

R1 changes the circuit conditions, and if it is set too close to the negative end, the lamp will not turn off. If it is too near the other end, the lamp will not turn on. With the values shown, the lamp is on for a period of about 2 or 3 seconds and off for a period of 4 to 5 seconds.. Capacitor C1 largely determines the period of this cycle, and increasing the value of C1 will increase the period of the cycle. The value of R5 also determines the time constant, but it should not be less than 250 ohms for a 6-volt supply.

It is possible to operate this circuit at 12 volts using two 6-volt lamps in series or one 12-volt lamp with a rating of between 0.15 and 0.25 amperes. Resistor R5 should not be less than 500 ohms, and resistors R3 and R4 should be made about twice the values shown in the circuit. The voltage rating of C1 must be 12 volts in this case.

REMOTE TEMPERATURE INDICATOR

Transistors are, of course, temperature-sensitive devices, and this remote temperature indicator takes advantage of the change in characteristics with an increase in temperature.

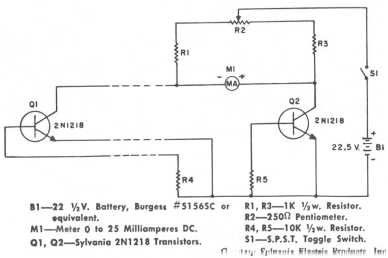

B1—22 ½V. Battery, Burgess #5156SC or equivalent.
M1—Meter 0 to 25 Milliamperes DC.
Q1, Q2—Sylvania 2N1218 Transistors.

R1, R3—1K ½w. Resistor.
R2—250Ω Pentiometer.
R4, R5—10K ½w. Resistor.
S1—S.P.S.T. Toggle Switch.

Remote temperature indicator circuit.

Essentially this is a bridge circuit with a transistor in each of the two legs and resistors (R1 and R3) in each of the other two legs. R2 is used for a balance control. A voltage is applied across the bridge and a meter is used to indicate bridge unbalance. In operation, Q1, which is a 2N1218 transistor, is connected by long leads and is the temperature-sensitive element. This transistor is placed at the remote point where the temperature is to be measured, and the degree of unbalance, as indicated on the meter, can be read directly as temperature.

The calibration of the instrument is accomplished by first setting the balance control (R2) so that the circuit is equalized. Remote transistor Q1 is then heated using an oven, and the face of the meter is calibrated in degrees. For each step the oven is first raised to a certain temperature and allowed to stablize. The actual temperature reading is measured using an ordinary thermometer, and this reading is then marked on the face of the meter. The temperature is increased, and the new reading is marked on the meter face. In this way it is possible to calibrate the instrument from about normal room temperature up to the range of 500°F.

AUTOMOBILE TACHOMETER

This tachometer for 12-volt systems indicates the automobile speed in rpm. Input is from a spark plug; C1 and C2 couple the sharp pulses. Because these spark pulses may have an amplitude of 10,000 volts, the input capacitors have a combined rating of 20,000 volts. R2 is adjusted to eliminate erratic behavior of the meter due to an overdrive from the input.

The circuit is a controlled (one-shot) multivibrator, where Q1 is normally on and Q2 is normally off. The negative pulses, which occur when the spark plug fires, trigger the multivibrator and cause Q1 to turn off and Q2 to conduct. The period of conduction is determined by the multivibrator RC time constant. The amount of current per pulse through the meter is controlled by potentiometer R11 in the collector circuit of Q2; this is used as a calibration control. Silicon diode CR2 is biased in the reverse direction and conducts only when the multivibrator fires due to a spark pulse.

Since there are two revolutions of the motor between successive firings of one specific spark plug, when the meter is calibrated to indicate 5000 rpm, the source of input pulses must be 2,500 pulses per minute for full-scale deflection.

For proper operation adjust signal-input control R2 until meter M1 smoothly indicates the rpm of the motor. Over-adjustment may cause erratic behavior of the meter.

Adjust R11 for full-scale deflection with an input rate of 2,500

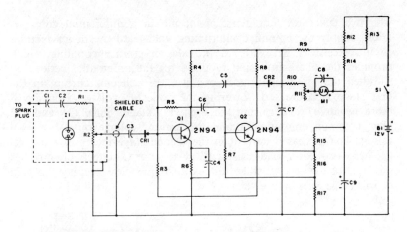

B1 - 12V. Battery of the automobile. See note in text for 6V. Battery.

C1, C2 - 500 mmf Capacitor, 10,000V. or greater.

C3 - .001 mfd Paper or Ceramic Disc Capacitor.

C4, C6 - 5 mfd Electrolytic, 6V. or greater.

C5 - .05 mfd Paper Capacitor.

C7, C9 - 50 mfd Electrolytic Capacitor, 12V. or greater.

C8 - 200 mfd Electrolytic Capacitor, 3V. or greater.

CR1 - Sylvania Diode, 1N34

CR2 - Sylvania Silicon Diode, 1N456.

I1 - Neon Lamp NE-2.

M1 - Meter, 0 to 50 Microamperes DC.

Q1, Q2 - Sylvania 2N94 Transistors (NPN type).

R1 - 1.5K 1/2w. Resistor.

R2, R11 - 2.5K Potentiometers.

R3, R4, R8 - 3.3K 1/2w. Resistor.

R5 - 22K 1/2w. Resistor.

R6, R7 - 2.2K 1/2w. Resistor.

R9 - 220Ω 1/2w. Resistor.

R10 - 1.0K 1/2w. Resistor.

R12, R13 - 120Ω 1/2w. Resistor.

R14 - 15Ω 1/2w. Resistor.

R15 - 33Ω 1/2w. Resistor.

R16 - 4.7Ω 1w. Resistor.

R17 - 10Ω 1/2w. Resistor.

S1 - S.P.S.T. Toggle Switch.

Courtesy Sylvania Electric Products, Inc.

Automobile-tachometer circuit.

pulses per minute. For 6-volt ignition systems, R12 and R13 are omitted and replaced with a short. Calibration can be by a square-wave generator or an actual engine using another tachometer.

AUDIO VOLTMETER

The audio voltmeter is a convenient piece of test equipment for the high-fidelity enthusiast or the home experimenter for the measurement of low-level audio signals. This circuit has a full-scale sensitivity of 10 mv rms, enabling the measurement of audio voltages as low as 1 mv rms with a reasonable degree of accuracy. Typical applications of the audio voltmeter include: frequency-response characteristics of audio power amplifiers; continuity in intercom networks; microphone-triggered circuits; and many other uses.

The audio voltmeter is a differential amplifier with the output rectified by a full-wave rectifier and applied to a DC meter movement. The applied, low-level audio signal is coupled through capacitors C1 and C3 to the bases of transistors Q1 and Q2, respectively.

The two transistor amplifiers, connected in a differential configuration, supply the amplified alternating voltage to the meter rectifier circuit. Resistors R5 and R6 provide an emitter coupling which provides the phase inversion required for the differential action.

When the input signal goes positive, the collector current in the first stage is decreased, lowering the collector voltage (making it more negative) and raising the emitter voltage. Since Q1 and Q2 have common emitter coupling, the emitter voltage on Q2 is also raised. The increased current in the second stage increases the voltage across collector load resistor R3. Capacitor C3 effectively grounds the base of the second stage for audio frequencies, keeping the gain of this stage at a high level.

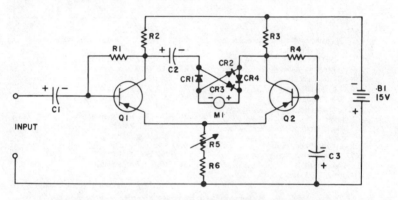

B1 — 15-volt battery
C1 — 10 mfd electrolytic capacitor, 25 volt
C2, C3 — 50 mfd electrolytic capacitor,
   25 volt
CR1, CR2, CR3, CR4 — Sylvania 1N34A diode

M1 — dc meter movement,
   100 microamperes full-scale
Q1, Q2 — Sylvania 2N1266 transistor
R1, R4 — 120 k, ½ w
R2, R3 — 6.8 k, ½ w
R5 — 1 k carbon potentiometer, ⅓ w or larger
R6 — 1.8 k, ½ w

Courtesy Sylvania Electric Products, Inc.

Audio-voltmeter circuit.

Calibration of the audio voltmeter is very simple, requiring only another meter which is already calibrated and connecting both meters to a common signal source at a frequency of about 1,000 cps. Resistor R5 is then adjusted so that the constructed meter reads the same as the calibrated meter. The meter has a response that is constant within 1 db from 17 cycles per second to 250 kilocycles per second and an input impedance of 1.2K ohms.

BRIDGE NULL DETECTOR

The bridge null detector is designed to be used in conjunction with a bridge circuit to obtain a more accurate null indication than could

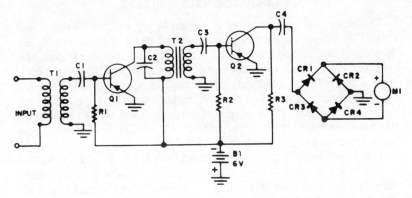

B1 — 6-volt battery	M1 — Meter, 200 microamperes full-scale
C1, C3 — 0.5 mfd paper, 100 volt	Q1, Q2 — Sylvania 2N1265 transistor
C2 — 0.002-0.005 mfd mica or ceramic disc, 100-volt	R1, R2 — 1 meg, ½ w
C4 — 0.25 mfd paper, 100-volt	R3 — 6.8 k, ½ w
CR1, CR2, CR3, CR4 — Sylvania 1N64 diodes	T1 — Stancor TA-24
	T2 — Stancor TA-27

Courtesy Sylvania Electric Products, Inc.

Bridge null-detector circuit.

normally be obtained from a conventional DC or AC meter. The degree of nulling which can be obtained in a bridge circuit is dependent on how small a null signal can be detected. The minimum null level that can be detected is determined by the sensitivity of the device being used to measure the null. This circuit is particularly well suited for this purpose, since it has both a sensitive output indication and a high-gain amplifier section. Combined, these permit measurement of an unbalance as low as 1 microvolt rms.

The null signal from the bridge circuit is coupled through transformer T1 and capacitor C1 to the base of grounded-emitter amplifier Q1. Capacitor C1 isolates the base bias on Q1 from T1. The amplified null signal from the collector of Q1 is coupled through transformer T2 and capacitor C3 to the base of grounded-emitter amplifier Q2. Capacitor C2 and the primary of T2 form a tuned tank to increase the collector impedance on Q1, thus increasing the gain of the first stage.

The amplified null signal from the collector of Q2 is developed across resistor R3 and coupled through capacitor C4 to full-wave rectifier circuit CR1 through CR4. The DC output from the full-wave rectifier drives the microammeter. The center frequency of the amplifier section is 700 cps. The 3-db points occur at 400 cps and 2kc. In order to obtain maximum sensitivity from the bridge null detector, it should be used with bridges which operate within this frequency range. The most commonly used frequency in bridge circuits is 1 kilocycle, which is ideal for this circuit.

TRANSISTOR-BETA CHECKER

The transistor beta checker is a simple yet extremely functional unit. This simple circuit has a minimum of parts and will readily indicate whether or not a transistor is functioning. A degenerative bias arrangement is used to compress a wide range of DC current gain values into a fairly small indicator scale. Gain indication is provided by an ordinary 1,000-ohm-per-volt meter movement on the 5-volt scale. It is essential that this type of meter be used on this scale since the 5K-ohm load which it presents to the circuit is calibrated into the voltage versus gain readings.

If a more sensitive movement is used, resistance should be shunted across its terminals to lower its impedance to 5K ohms. If a vacuum-tube voltmeter is used, the value for the shunt resistance is exactly 5K ohms since the impedance of the meter itself is several megohms. Battery-reversing switch S1 enables measurement of both NPN and PNP transistors. The circuit is drawn in the correct way for testing NPN transistors. When testing PNP transistors, reverse the meter leads on meter M1 and place S1 in the PNP position. The transistor beta checker will work with all but the larger heat-sink type transistors.

The meter indication on M1 is directly proportional to the battery voltage in addition to varying with DC beta; therefore a fresh bat-

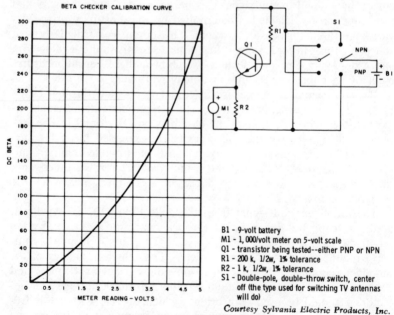

B1 - 9-volt battery
M1 - 1,000/volt meter on 5-volt scale
Q1 - transistor being tested--either PNP or NPN
R1 - 200 k, 1/2w, 1% tolerance
R2 - 1 k, 1/2w, 1% tolerance
S1 - Double-pole, double-throw switch, center off (the type used for switching TV antennas will do)

Courtesy Sylvania Electric Products, Inc.

Circuit for transistor-beta checker.

tery must be used. A battery of slightly higher or lower voltage can be used, provided that the meter indication is corrected. If a 10.5-volt battery is used, for instance, it is 16.7% higher than the 9-volt value. Therefore the meter indication will be 16.7% higher than the value which would be obtained with a 9-volt battery. The DC beta may be determined from the graph.

APPLAUSE METER

The applause meter is a useful tool for judging many types of competitive sports events and contests. Many people would dispute a judge's decision of which group shouted and applauded the loudest, but few will dare challenge an electronic applause meter. The applause meter can also be useful without the speaker as a high-gain amplifier and indicator to give relative indications of low-level input signals.

Speaker SP1 is utilized as a microphone to convert the applause sound waves into electrical energy to drive coupling transformer T1. The applause signal is coupled through T1 and capacitor C1 to the base of audio amplifier Q1. The setting of gain potentiometer R1 determines the amount of signal to be coupled to Q1. Transistors Q1, Q2, and Q3 comprise a three-stage, capacitor-coupled audio amplifier. Resistor R4 is the collector load resistor Q1, and resistor R2 is a biasing resistor. Audio amplifier stages Q2 and Q3 are identical to Q1. The amplified applause signal from the collector of Q3 is coupled through capacitor C4 to full-wave rectifier CR1 through CR4. The rectified applause signal is applied across meter M1 to give a comparative sound-level reading.

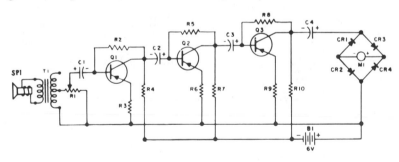

B1 — 6-volt battery
C1, C2, C3, C4 — 10 mfd electrolytic, 25-volt
CR1, CR2, CR3, CR4 — Sylvania 1N64 diode
LS1 — 3-6 ohm loudspeaker
M1 — 1 milliampere full-scale meter

Q1, Q2, Q3 — Sylvania 2N1265 transistor
R1 — 5 k, ½ w potentiometer
R2, R5, R8 — 150 k, ½ w
R3, R6, R9 — 100 Ω, ½ w
R4, R7, R10 — 8.8 k, ½ w
T1 — Stancor TA-33 or equivalent

Applause-meter circuit.

In the construction of the applause meter it is advisable to place the speaker pickup on the opposite side from the meter to facilitate ease of reading while the speaker pickup is pointed directly at the cheering crowd. To be fair to all concerned when monitoring applause, it is essential that the speaker be aimed at the center of each spectator group being monitored. The gain potentiometer should not be changed for a given set of readings.

AUDIO PHOTOMETER

The audio photometer is a light-sensitive oscillator whose frequency varies with the intensity of the light illuminating the sun battery. This device is useful for audio monitoring of such things as lights on or off in remote rooms, doors open or closed, etc. The advantage of the audio photometer over conventional light-sensitive devices is that it does not require visual monitoring; thus, one can be free to read, work, or do many other things while monitoring the audible output of the circuit. Also, the ear is more sensitive to small changes in audio frequency than the eye is to light intensity.

The audio photometer consists of three grounded-emitter amplifiers having positive feedback connections to form an oscillator circuit. The output from the collector of grounded-emitter amplifier Q1 is coupled through capacitor C2 to the base of Q2. Resistor R2 is the collector load resistor. The output of grounded-emitter amplifier Q2 is coupled through capacitor C3 to the base of Q3 and through feedback capacitor C1 to the base of Q1. Since a single

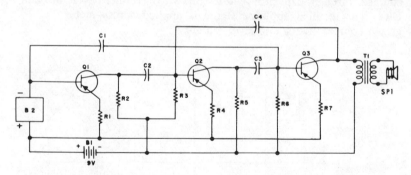

B1 — 9-volt battery	LS1 — 3-6 ohm loudspeaker
B2 — Sun battery, International Rectifier Corp. Type B2M or equivalent	Q1, Q2, Q3 — Sylvania 2N1264 transistor
	R1 — 390 Ω, ½ w
C1, C3 — 0.1 mfd ceramic disc or paper, 50-volt	R2, R5 — 10 k, ½ w
	R3, R6 — 100 k, ½ w
C2 — 0.02 mfd ceramic disc or paper, 50-volt	R4, R7 — 47 Ω, ½ w
C4 — 0.05 mfd ceramic disc or paper, 50-volt	T1 — Thordarson TR-29 or equivalent

Courtesy Sylvania Electric Products, Inc.

Audio-photometer circuit.

grounded-emitter amplifier stage produces a phase shift of 180°, two stages will produce a phase shift of 360°. Thus, the signal from the collector of Q2 is 360° out of phase with the signal at the base of Q1, providing a positive feedback signal to Q1. This positive feedback signal causes Q1 and Q2 to act as an oscillator pair. The signal from the collector of Q3 is coupled through capacitor C4 to the base of Q2 as a positive feedback signal similar to the oscillator pair Q1 and Q2. The resulting signal from the collector of Q3 is coupled through transformer T1 to speaker SP1 as an audible tone. Emitter resistors R1, R4, and R7 stabilize the gain of the three stages. The frequency of oscillation is determined by small phase shifts which are developed through the amplifier stages by the various resistors and capacitors.

When the intensity of light on the sun battery changes, the bias current supplied to transistor Q1 also changes. This changes the input and output impedances of the first stage, changing the phase shifts involved in that part of the circuit and changing the oscillator frequency of the audio photometer.

IMPEDANCE METER

A device for measuring the relative impedance of circuit elements is extremely useful; this circuit is a grounded emitter amplifier the output of which is used to drive the milliammeter which is in series with R2. A 1.5-volt source is used, and bias current is provided for the transistor by passing this current through the impedance to be measured.

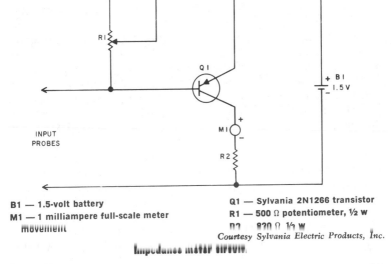

B1 — 1.5-volt battery
M1 — 1 milliampere full-scale meter
movement

Q1 — Sylvania 2N1266 transistor
R1 — 500 Ω potentiometer, ½ w
R2 — 820 Ω ½ w

Courtesy Sylvania Electric Products, Inc.

Impedance meter circuit.

Clearly, any changes in the impedance will cause changes in the bias current. Also, the collector current that passes through the milliammeter will show the change in impedance because the collector current is a function of the bias current.

Potentiometer R1 is the sensitivity adjustment used for shunting bias current for the transistor. Through the use of this control, sensitivity can be decreased or increased to measure various values of impedance. This circuit can be used for troubleshooting since it will indicate relative impedances by variations in current flow. If resistor R1 is effectively out of the circuit (infinite resistance), this unit will measure impedances as high as 1 megohm. When used for measuring an unknown impedance source, the sensitivity adjustment (R1) should always be set so that its resistance is the minimum possible. The resistance is slowly increased until a measurable reading is obtained on the meter. This, then, is the measure of the relative impedance of the circuit being tested.

METAL LOCATOR

The metal locator comes in handy for locating wall studs or metal piping, and it can even be used to locate wiring within the wall. The metal locator could also be used for finding small screws or washers that are lost in a rug or outdoors in the grass as well as many other uses.

The metal locator is based on the principle of two high-frequency signals of approximately the same frequency being beat together to produce an audio signal. When the pick-up coil of one of the high-frequency oscillators is placed near a ferromagnetic material, the inductance of the coil is changed. Since the pick-up coil is part of the oscillator tank circuit, the oscillator frequency changes and the difference frequency produced by the mixing of the two high-frequency signals also changes. When properly tuned, the two oscillators operate on almost exactly the same frequency, thus producing a beat signal having a very low frequency. Now an audio signal is heard only when the pickup coil is placed near a ferromagnetic material.

Transistor Q1 is a high-frequency oscillator with capacitors C2 and C3 and pickup coil L1 forming the tank circuit. Resistors R1 and R2 provide base bias for Q1. Regenerative feedback is applied to the emitter of Q1. The output of Q1 is taken from the collector and coupled through capacitor C4 to the base of oscillator Q2. Resistors R4 and R5 provide base bias for Q2. The two high-frequency signals are mixed in Q2.

The resulting audio signal from the collector of Q2 is coupled through capacitor C8 to the base of audio amplifier Q3. The audio signal is developed across resistor R7, amplified by Q3, and applied

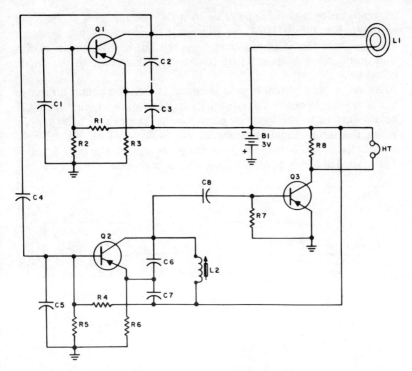

B1 — 3-volt battery
C1, C5 — 0.001 mfd ceramic disc or paper
C2 — 0.02 mfd ceramic disc or paper
C3, C8 — 0.01 mfd ceramic disc or paper
C4 — 100 mmfd disc or mica
C6 — 0.002 mfd ceramic disc or mica
C7 — 0.001 mfd ceramic disc or mica

HT — Crystal or 2 kohm headphones
L1 — 14 turns of #18 enameled wire,
 5½" dia., scramble wound
L2 — 20 mh, slug-tuned
Q1, Q2, Q3 — Sylvania 2N1266 transistor
R1, R2, R4, R5, R8 — 5.1 k, ½ w
R3, R6 — 330 Ω, ½ w
R7 — 3.3 meg, ½ w

Courtesy Sylvania Electric Products, Inc.

Metal-locater circuit.

to the headset (HT). Resistor R8 is the collector load resistor. The slug of coil L2 is adjusted so that a low-frequency growl is heard in the earphones. If metal is now placed near pick-up coil L1, it will increase the inductance and lower the frequency of the variable oscillator, causing the audio frequency to increase.

LAMP DRIVER

Controlled rectifiers (SCR's) are useful as lamp drivers where they control incandescent lamps from small DC signals or low-level pulses.

Circuit A utilizes the inherent bistable "memory" characteristic of the SCR when used with a DC voltage supply. The SCR can be triggered on by a positive pulse or by a DC voltage level at the input terminal. For the 3B1034 the triggering requirements are 2 ma at 2 volts. Once the SCR has been triggered on, it will remain in this state until it has been reset by momentarily inetrrupting the anode current.

An AC supply system is used in circuit B, and the circuit no longer has memory. When a DC signal is applied to the input, the SCR passes current to the lamp on each positive half-cycle of the supply. When the input signal is removed, the SCR turns off on the subsequent negative half-cycle, remaining off until an input signal is again applied. This SCR is acting like a high-gain power transistor

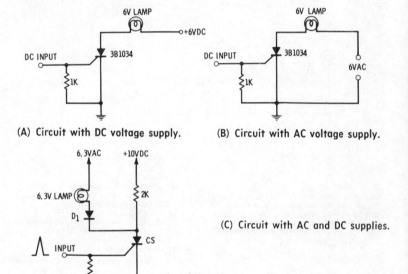

(A) Circuit with DC voltage supply.   (B) Circuit with AC voltage supply.

(C) Circuit with AC and DC supplies.

Courtesy Solid State Products, Inc.
Lamp-driver circuit.

with the additional advantage of eliminating a DC power supply for the lamp circuit.

Circuit C illustrates memory action by combining DC and AC supplies, providing two advantages. The lamp power is obtained from the AC supply, reducing the DC power requirements. Only a small amount (5 to 10 ma) of DC load current is necessary to hold controlled switch CS on when the AC supply is negative. To turn CS off, it is necessary only to interrupt the relatively small amount of DC flowing to the anode of CS through the circuit branch containing the 2K-ohm resistor.

DIFFERENTIAL VOLTAGE-LEVEL INDICATOR

The differential voltage-level indicator is an electronic device used to monitor line or test voltages. When the voltage goes above or below a predetermined level, one of two indicator lamps is illuminated, indicating whether the voltage is high or low. By adding the proper circuits to the outputs, this sensing circuit can be used for control, as well as for indication. By selection of the proper zener voltage levels, resistors, lamps, etc. this circuit may be used over a wide range of voltages.

The voltage to be monitored is applied to the input, rectified by diode D1, filtered by capacitor C1, and applied to zener diode Z1.

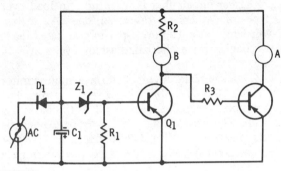

FUNCTION:

AC INPUT 6 VOLTS TO 7 VOLTS.

A IS ILLUMINATED AND B EXTINGUISHED AT 6 VOLTS.

B IS ILLUMINATED AND A EXTINGUISHED AT 7 VOLTS.

CIRCUIT VALUES

D_1 - 1N2610	R_1 - 1KΩ, 1/2 WATT
Z_1 - 1N3016	R_2 - 47Ω, 1/2 WATT
Q_1, Q_2 - 2N1191	R_3 - 5KΩ, 1/2 WATT
C_1 - 2000mfd 15V.	A, B - GE #48 OR EQUIV. - 2V 60 Ma.

Courtesy Motorola Semiconductor Products, Inc.

Circuit of differential voltage-level indicator.

When DC voltages are being monitored, diode D1 and capacitor C1 are not used. This circuit is designed for a nominal voltage of 6 volts with the parts values given in the parts list. In this particular circuit 5.5 volts AC holds lamp A on, whereas raising the supply level to 6.5 volts AC turns lamp A off and lamp B on.

At voltages lower than the zener voltage of Z1, no base current is applied to transistor Q1, thus holding it cut off. The negative collector voltage of Q1 furnishes base current to Q2, driving Q2 into conduction and illuminating lamp A. When the supply voltage exceeds the zener level of Z1, Q1 starts conducting, illuminating lamp

63

B. The drop in collector voltage on Q1 cuts off Q2 and extinguishes lamp A.

Voltage-level indicator and control circuits using zener diodes for voltage reference and transistors for functional control offer a large field of application in both commercial and industrial areas. The simple circuit described provides one way a differential indication can be obtained.

100-CYCLE-PER-MINUTE FLASHER

This 12-volt, 100-cycle-per-minute flasher circuit gives a method of obtaining a flasher circuit that is insensitive to load over a large range. Two types of flashers are discussed, one (A) drives a single bank of 12-volt lamps at a 100-cycle-per-minute rate, and the other (B) drives two banks which alternate flashing cycles at a 100-cycle-per-minute rate.

Transistors Q1 and Q2 in circuit A form a multivibrator circuit. When Q1 conducts, the collector voltage rises sharply. The sudden voltage rise is coupled through capacitor C1 to the base of transistor Q2, cutting it off. The base voltage on Q2 drops exponentially until Q2 again starts conducting. When Q2 conducts, its collector voltage rises sharply. The sudden voltage rise is coupled through capacitor

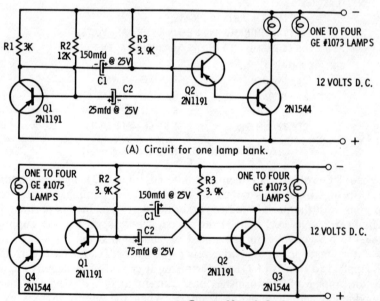

(A) Circuit for one lamp bank.

Courtesy Motorola Semiconductor Products, Inc.

(B) Circuit for two lamp banks.

100-cycle-per-minute flasher circuits.

C2 to the base of Q1, cutting it off. The multivibrator action produces a 100-cycle-per-minute square wave. The frequency of the square-wave output is determined by the resistance from the base to the negative side of the battery and by the value of the capacitors. Therefore the time constant is not dependent on the lamps and you may use from one to four lamps without affecting the frequency. Transistor Q3 provides the necessary current to light the lamps. When Q2 is conducting, the base current of Q3 increases, driving Q3 into conduction. The outputs of Q2 and Q3 are connected in parallel.

Circuit B is basically the same as circuit A except the input circuit has been changed to provide another bank of lights which will flash alternately with the bank of lights connected to the collectors of Q2 and Q3. The lamps in the collector circuit of Q1 and Q4 are the collector load. Transistor Q4 provides the additional current required to illuminate the bank of lamps.

Either circuit can easily be mounted in a $3 \times 3 \times 2$ inch metal box using the box as a heat sink for the power transistors (Q3 and Q4). Power dissipation is at a minimum in the circuit since the transistors operate either at saturation or cutoff.

FLASHER CIRCUIT

The flasher circuit is essentially a saturated astable (free-running) multivibrator used to operate switching transistor Q1, which turns lamp L1 on and off. By using low values of capacitance the physical

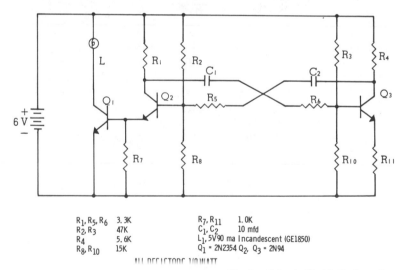

R_1, R_5, R_6	3. 3K	R_7, R_{11}	1. 0K
R_2, R_3	47K	C_1, C_2	10 mfd
R_4	5. 6K	L_1, 5V 90 ma Incandescent (GE1850)	
R_8, R_{10}	15K	Q_1 = 2N2354 Q_2, Q_3 = 2N94	

ALL RESISTORS 1/2 WATT

Courtesy Sylvania Electric Products, Inc.

Flasher circuit.

size of the capacitor can be kept small, thus keeping the overall circuit size down. For this reason the resistive elements become the frequency controllers. Much lower frequencies are possible with larger values of capacitance. The duty cycle of the flasher circuit may be easily altered by manipulation of the values of resistors R5 and R6 and capacitors C1 and C2. Using the component values given in the parts list, the flasher unit produces between 2 and 3 pulses per second.

Transistors Q2 and Q3 form the active part of the astable multivibrator. Assuming Q2 is conducting when the circuit is turned on, its collector voltage rises sharply. The sudden voltage rise is coupled through capacitor C1 and resistor R6 to the base of Q3, cutting off Q3. The base voltage on Q3 drops exponentially until it again starts conducting. When Q3 starts to conduct, its collector voltage rises sharply. The sudden voltage rise is coupled through capacitor C2 and resistor R5 to the base of Q2. The RC time constant of C2-R5 and C1-R6 determines the frequency of the multivibrator output. The output of the multivibrator is taken from the emitter of Q2. By not placing the lamp directly in the multivibrator cricuit, smaller values of capacitance and larger values of emitter resistors can be used, resulting in better circuit stability. The multivibrator signal is applied to the base of switching transistor Q1, alternately causing it to conduct and be cut off. The alternate conduction of Q1 in series with lamp L1 results in a flashing light.

TRANSIENT-VOLTAGE INDICATOR

The transient voltage indicator is a simple, compact instrument which can be used for solving a major portion of the transient voltage problems normally associated with semiconductors. Some of the uses of the transient voltage indicator include checking severity of voltage transients in systems where semiconductor equipment is to be installed, developing statistical data on voltage transients for various types of power systems, determining the effectiveness of transient energy storage and filtering circuits, isolating sources of voltage transients, etc. The user presets a level of voltage on the precision potentiometer dial. If this instantaneous voltage is exceeded, the circuit energizes the indicating lamp which remains lit until the circuit is reset by the push button on the panel.

The circuit employs a unijunction transistor (Q1) to compare the input signal with the reference and to actuate the tripping and latching circuits. The input signal at which the unijunction transistor trips is set by potentiometer R1. When the unijunction trips, it fires a silicon-controlled rectifier (SCR), thereby actuating latching relay LR1 and lighting indicating lamp I1 in a separate low-voltage circuit. At

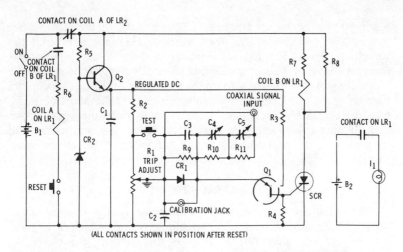

CONTACT ON COIL A OF LR$_2$

REGULATED DC

COAXIAL SIGNAL INPUT

(ALL CONTACTS SHOWN IN POSITION AFTER RESET)

SCR - GE C11F CONTROLLED RECTIFIER
Q$_1$ - GE 2N1671B UNIJUNCTION TRANSISTOR
Q$_2$ - GE 2N167 TRANSISTOR
CR$_1$ - 1N645 RECTIFIER
CR$_2$ - 1N1317 ZENER DIODE - 150 MW, 17-21V
B$_1$ - 22 1/2 VOLT BATTERY, BURGESS 4156
B$_2$ - 1 1/2 VOLT BATTERY, BURGESS 2FBP

R$_1$ - 50,000Ω HELIPOT, SERIES C, 3 TURN

R$_2$ - 4700Ω 1/2 WATT
R$_3$ - 470Ω 1/2 WATT
R$_4$ - 100Ω 1/2 WATT
R$_5$ - 4700Ω 1/2 WATT
R$_6$, R$_7$ - 47Ω 1 WATT
R$_8$ - 220Ω 1 WATT
R$_9$ - 2500Ω 1 WATT, 1% TOLERANCE
R$_{10}$, R$_{11}$ - 499,000Ω 1 WATT 1% TOLERANCE

LR$_1$ - POTTER-BRUMFIELD LATCHING RELAY
          TYPE KE 17D-12V DC
I$_1$ - GE TYPE 49 LAMP BULB, .06A, 2 VOLTS
C$_1$ - 100 MFD, 50V DC ELECTROLYTIC CAPACITOR
C$_2$ - 2.0 MFD, 200V DC PAPER CAPACITOR
C$_3$ - 2000 MMF MICA CAPACITOR
C$_4$, C$_5$ - 1 TO 7.5 MMF CERAMIC TRIMMER
          CAPACITORS

Courtesy General Electric Co.

Circuit of transient-voltage indicator.

the same time, the latching relay disconnects the tripping circuit from its battery to shut off the controlled rectifier and conserve battery energy. Depressing the reset button energizes the other coil in the latching relay, extinguishing the lamp and readying the circuit for the next trip. Transistor Q2 in conjunction with reference diode CR2 applies a regulated DC voltage to the unijunction transistor and its bias circuit. Thus battery-voltage fluctuations due to aging do not affect the accuracy of the circuit until the battery voltage drops below the avalanche voltage of CR2. The voltage signal to be monitored by the equipment is introduced at the coaxial signal input and, depending on the desired voltage range of the instrument, is stepped down by a suitable voltage divider. In this circuit the signal introduced to the unijunction circuit across resistor R9 is 1/400th of the input voltage, having been stepped down by the RC network consisting of R9, R10, R11, C3, C4, and C5. Capacitor C2 provides sufficient energy for firing the SCR. When Q1 triggers, C2 discharges through diode CR1, Q1, and resistor R4. In order to maintain the dividing ratio of the step-down network at all frequencies, capacitors C3, C4, and C5 are connected across their respective resistors. Capacitors C4 and C5 are trimmed to secure uniform response of the network to all frequencies. Trimming these capacitors is accomplished by apply ing a 100-kc, or higher frequency, square wave to the signal-input terminals of the divider and then adjusting the capacitors until the waveshape across R9 appears identical in shape to the input waveform. A calibration chart correlating the input signal voltage and the dial setting of R1 necessary to produce tripping of the equipment can now be prepared. Using a high-voltage supply, calibration of R1 is best performed by applying a known voltage into the signal input jack. If only a low-voltage supply is available, the low voltage can be applied to the calibration jack and multiplied by the divider ratio to determine the corresponding voltage at the signal input.

ALARM CIRCUIT

The alarm circuit is essentially a saturated astable (free-running) multivibrator used to operate a switching transistor which turns lamp L1 on and off. However, as long as the contacts are closed on switch SW, transistor Q4 is saturated, and the base of transistor Q2 is essentially grounded, preventing the flasher circuit from operating. The alarm circuit could be used for a number of applications, such as a warning that a door or window has been opened, or as a safety device indicating that a car door is not shut tight, and so on.

Transistors Q2 and Q3 form the active part of the astable multivibrator circuit. Transistor Q4 effectively grounds the base of Q2 when switch SW is closed, preventing the multivibrator circuit from operating. When switch SW is open, the positive bias is removed

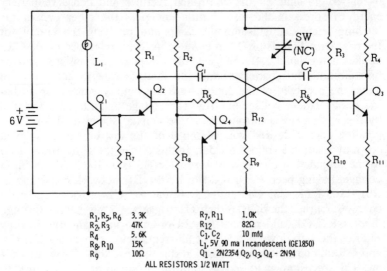

R_1, R_5, R_6	3.3K	R_7, R_{11}	1.0K
R_2, R_3	47K	R_{12}	82Ω
R_4	5.6K	C_1, C_2	10 mfd
R_8, R_{10}	15K	L_1, 5V 90 ma Incandescent (GE1850)	
R_9	10Ω	Q_1 - 2N2354 Q_2, Q_3, Q_4 - 2N94	

ALL RESISTORS 1/2 WATT

Courtesy Sylvania Electric Products, Inc.

Alarm circuit.

from the base of Q4, and ceases to conduct. The base of Q2 is now properly biased to cause Q2 and Q3 to function as an astable multivibrator. Assuming Q2 is conducting more heavily than Q3 when Q4 is cut off, the collector voltage on Q2 will rise sharply. This sudden voltage rise is coupled through capacitor C1 and resistor R6 to the base of Q3, cutting off Q3. The base voltage on Q3 drops exponentially until it again starts conducting. When Q3 starts to conduct, its collector voltage rises sharply. The sudden voltage. rise is coupled through capacitor C2 and resistor R5 to the base of Q2, cutting Q2 off. The base voltage on Q2 drops exponentially until it again starts conducting. When Q2 starts to conduct, Q3 is cut off, thus completing the cycle. The RC time constant of C2-R5 and C1-R6 determines the frequency of the multivibrator output. The output signal from the emitter of Q2 is applied to the base of switching transistor Q1. The multivibrator output alternately switches Q1 on and off, causing lamp L1 to flash on and off.

DIGITAL TEMPERATURE INDICATOR

In the digital temperature indicator a temperature-sensitive thermistor is used to control the current through a voltage divider and, consequently, the voltage dropped across each half of the voltage divider. The circuit uses two neon lamps to indicate the temperature range of the ambient air. The digital temperature indicator can indicate relative temperature (cold-warm-hot) from 110°C to 150°C. When the relative temperature is cold, only lamp L1 is illuminated. When the relative temperature is warm, both lamps L1 and L2 are illuminated. When the relative temperature is hot, only lamp L2 is illuminated.

To adjust the digital temperature indicator, maintain the thermistor at the desired temperature and adjust warm-adjust resistor

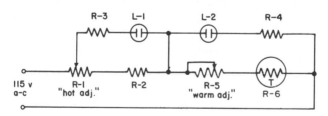

R-1 - 2,500-ohm potentiometer, 4 watts
R-2 - 3,600-ohm resistor
R-3, R-4 - 15K resistor
R-5 - 4,000-ohm potentiometer, 4 watts
L 1, L 2 NE 51 bulb
R-6 - thermistor type 802-1 or 802-5

Courtesy Westinghouse Electric Corp.
Circuit of digital temperature indicator.

R5 so that lamp L2 just lights. Now, with the thermistor still maintained at the desired temperature, adjust hot adjust resistor R1 so that lamp L1 will just turn off.

When the digital temperature indicator is properly adjusted, the resistance in parallel with neon lamp L2 will be lower than the resistance in parallel with neon lamp L1 if the ambient air temperature is cold. This is due to the temperature coefficient of thermistor R6. The resistance of R6 is directly proportional to the temperature. Since the same current flows through R1, R2, R5, and R6, a larger voltage is dropped across L1 than across L2. The higher voltage is just sufficient to illuminate L1. When the ambient temperature becomes warm, the resistance of thermistor R6 increases just enough so that the resistance in parallel with each lamp is the same. Therefore the same voltage will be dropped across each lamp and both of them will be illuminated. When the temperature becomes hot, the resistance across L2 becomes greater than the resistance across L1, and only lamp L2 is illuminated.

LIQUID-LEVEL INDICATOR

The liquid-level indicator uses a temperature-sensitive thermistor that is immersed in liquid as the liquid-level sensor. With thermistor R10 immersed in the liquid, indicator lamp L1 is illuminated. If the liquid level drops below the thermistor, the resistance of the thermistor is increased, causing indicator lamp L1 to extinguish and indicator lamp L2 to be illuminated. When the liquid level drops below the thermistor level, there is a 10- to 30-second delay before low indicator lamp L2 illuminates. When the liquid level rises above the thermistor level, there is a 2- to 10-second time delay before normal

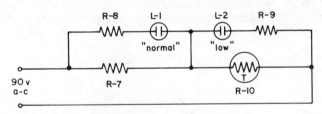

R-7 - 500-ohm resistor, 25 watts, for R-10
        equal to 802-1*
    - 450-ohm resistor, 25 watts, for R-10
        equal to 802-5*
R-8, R-9 - 15K resistor
L-1, L-2 - NE-51 bulb
R-10 - thermistor type 802-1 or 802-5
* approx value for motionless water or oil at 25°C

Courtesy Westinghouse Electric Corp.

Circuit of liquid-level indicator.

indicator lamp L1 illuminates. Both lamps are extinguished from 1 to 5 seconds during the transition period.

When thermistor R10 is immersed in liquid, its resistance is relatively low and more voltage is dropped across resistor R7 than across the thermistor. This high voltage across R7 is sufficient to illuminate neon lamp L1. When the liquid level drops below the thermistor, its resistance increases and more voltage is dropped across it than across R7. Thus neon lamp L2 is illuminated and L1 is extinguished. Due to the fairly slow temperature change of the thermistor, there is a slight delay encountered in the operation of the indicator lights.

HIGH-POWER ELECTRONIC FLASHER

Flasher circuits for incandescent lamps are widely used in a variety of applications, such as traffic lights, navigational beacons, aircraft beacons, and illuminated signs. This circuit has been chosen to illustrate the basic principles of a silicon-controlled–rectifier (SCR) flasher that can be easily simplified or modified to meet specific application requirements. It operates a lamp load up to 3 amperes over a supply voltage range of 17 to 35 volts. The circuit is basically a parallel inverter with capacitor commutation. The SCR's conduct alternately and are triggered by the free-running, unijunction-transistor (UJT) relaxation oscillator. The frequency of

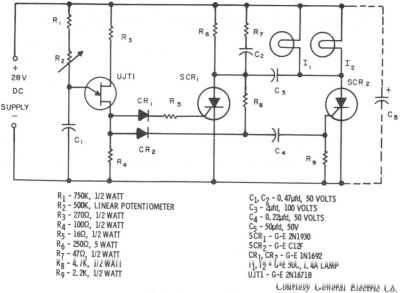

R_1 - 750K, 1/2 WATT
R_2 - 500K, LINEAR POTENTIOMETER
R_3 - 270Ω, 1/2 WATT
R_4 - 100Ω, 1/2 WATT
R_5 - 16Ω, 1/2 WATT
R_6 - 250Ω, 5 WATT
R_7 - 47Ω, 1/2 WATT
R_8 - 4.7K, 1/2 WATT
R_9 - 2.2K, 1/2 WATT

C_1, C_2 - 0.47μfd, 50 VOLTS
C_3 - 2μfd, 100 VOLTS
C_4 - 0.22μfd, 50 VOLTS
C_5 - 50μfd, 50V
SCR_1 - G-E 2N1930
SCR_2 - G-E C12F
CR_1, CR_2 - G-E 1N1692
I_1, I_2 - G-E 90C, 1.4A LAMP
UJT1 - G-E 2N1671B

Courtesy General Electric Co.

Circuit of high-power electronic flasher.

the relaxation is determined by the RC time constant of R1, R2, and C1 any may be adjusted to the value desired by means of potentiometer R2.

When power is applied to the circuit, capacitor C1 charges through resistors R1 and R2 until it reaches the emitter-base 1 breakdown voltage of unijunction transistor UJT1. UJT1 now fires, and C1 discharges through resistor R4 and UJT1, producing a positive pulse across R4. Assuming both controlled rectifiers SCR1 and SCR2 are off, diode CR2 has approximately 28 volts on its cathode, reverse-biasing it and hence blocking the trigger pulse at R4 from passing. The trigger pulse at R4 passes to the gate of SCR1, switching SCR1 on. Current flows through SCR1 and resistor R6. Capacitor C1 now recharges through R1 and R2, producing another positive pulse across R4. This positive triggering pulse is passed by CR2 since the cathode voltage on CR2 is essentially the same as the anode voltage of SCR1 which is conducting. The positive triggering pulse is coupled through capacitor C4 to the gate of SCR2, switching it on. The sudden decrease in anode voltage on SCR2 when it starts to conduct is coupled through commutating capacitor C3 to the anode of SCR1, switching SCR1 off. Lamps I1 and I2 are now lit by the current through SCR2 and the lamps. Since SCR1 is again cut off, the voltage at the cathode of CR2 is again approximately 28 volts and the next triggering pulse will be blocked by CR2. Thus SCR1 and SCR2 alternately conduct on successive pulses from relaxation oscillator UJT1.

LIGHT FLASHER

This circuit shows a light flasher that can be used for road-repair warning lights or for buoys. A pair of power transistors is used and,

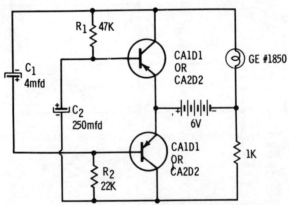

Courtesy Minneapolis-Honeywell Regulator Co.
Light-flasher circuit.

with the components shown, the frequency is 60 pulses per minute with an on-time of 80 milliseconds. There is 100 milliamperes of current with the lamp on. The repetition rate can be decreased and the time on lengthened by an increase in the values of R1, R2, or C1. To a lesser extent this also applies to C2. It is possible to change these values and to change both the power dissipation and the time on.

FLIP-FLOPS

COMPLEMENTARY FLIP-FLOP CIRCUIT

This circuit shows a complementary flip-flop using 2N782 and 2N783 transistors. A trigger input is applied to either A or B, with either positive- or negative-going input pulses. If a positive pulse is applied to A, it will turn on Q1 and turn off Q2. The bases of Q3 and Q4 are coupled to the collectors of Q1 and Q2 through RC networks. When Q3 goes toward cutoff and Q4 goes toward saturation, Q1 is driven on and Q2 is driven off; thus in this way transistor pairs Q1 and Q4 and Q2 and Q3 will alternately be on and off when the input is triggered by a series of pulses. Illustration B shows the input and output waveforms for four different frequencies.

This circuit can be used for various high-speed clock generators, logic circuits of different types, and industrial control circuits. It is capable of producing output pulses at rates as high as 10 mc. At 100 kc, the output amplitude shown is 16 volts using a 3-volt, square-wave triggering pulse. At 250 kc a higher amplitude trigger of 4 volts is required. For frequencies below 1 mc the supply voltage is 8 volts. At frequencies above 1 mc, the supply voltage can be reduced to 4 volts.

In an ordinary flip-flop, some of the signal output power is dissipated in the collector circuit resistors, but if this resistor is replaced by a complementary transistor as shown in the illustration, the power losses are reduced, and the power efficiency is increased. This becomes significant when all of the available output power from each stage is used as in systems using a number of stages. Another advantage of this type of flip-flop over the conventional type is that it is less critical with respect to supply-voltage variations.

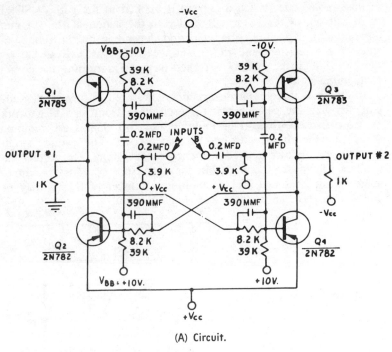

(A) Circuit.

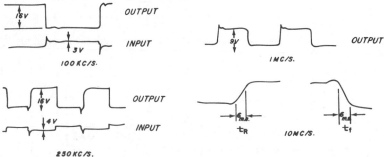

100 KC/S.

250 KC/S.

1 MC/S.

10 MC/S.

Courtesy Sylvania Electric Products, Inc.

(B) Waveforms.

Complementary flip-flop.

THREE-STAGE, SCR, FREE-RUNNING MULTIVIBRATOR

Silicon-controlled rectifiers have a large power handling capacity; because of this they are well suited as active elements in multivibrators for direct switching of loads. A three-stage, free-running multivibrator based on the monostable circuit may be constructed.

The monostable multivibrator in circuit A has two rectifiers and a diode; when it is turned on, SCR2 conducts and the circuit stays in this stable state. When a current is applied to the gate of SCR1 to turn it on, SCR2 is turned off due to the action of the 0.1-mfd commutating capacitor. After a period depending on the time constant of the resistors and the 0.5-mfd capacitor as well as the required firing current, SCR2 is turned on again, returning the circuit to its initial state.

In circuit B three controlled rectifiers are used to form a ring circuit, deriving the gate current for each stage from an RC network as shown. In the three-stage multivibrator two clamps are required to operate the circuit with one on and two off. The circuit is self-starting and follows a fixed sequence of operation. The timing capacitors shown are 0.5 mfd; but they need not be equal. A three-stage circuit is shown, but an unlimited number of SCR's may be coupled to form an n-stage, free-running circuit.

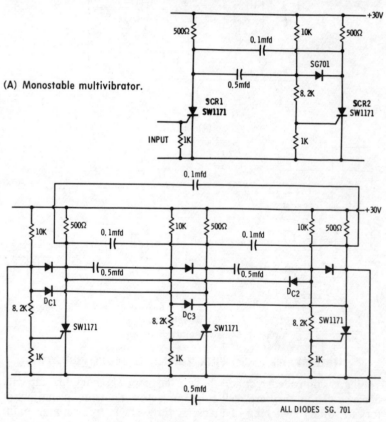

(A) Monostable multivibrator.

Courtesy Transitron Electronic Corp.
(B) Three-stage, free-running multivibrator.
Multivibrator circuits.

ALIGNMENT MULTIVIBRATOR

The alignment multivibrator is a free-running multivibrator that generates a square-wave output of about 700 cps. An emitter-follower stage is used to reduce loading on the multivibrator section and also to provide a low impedance for the square-wave output. Alternately conducting transistors Q1 and Q2 form the active part of the multivibrator circuit.

When transistor Q1 fires, its collector voltage rises sharply. The sudden voltage rise is coupled through capacitor C1 and resistors R3 and R6 to the base of transistor Q2, cutting it off. The base voltage on Q2 drops expotentially until Q2 again conducts. When Q2 fires, its collector voltage rises sharply. The sudden voltage rise is coupled through capacitor C2 and resistors R4 and R5 to the base of Q1 thus cutting off Q1. Resistors R1 and R8 are the collector load resistors for Q1 and Q2 respectively. Capacitor C3 shapes the pulse from the collector of Q2 and couples the pulse to the base of emitter-follower transistor Q3. Resistor R9 is a parasitic suppressor. Base bias for Q3 is developed across resistor R10.

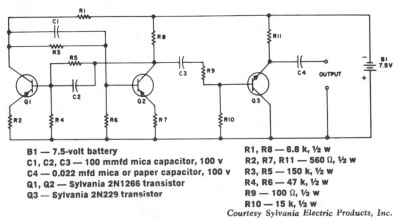

B1 — 7.5-volt battery	R1, R8 — 6.8 k, ½ w
C1, C2, C3 — 100 mmfd mica capacitor, 100 v	R2, R7, R11 — 560 Ω, ½ w
C4 — 0.022 mfd mica or paper capacitor, 100 v	R3, R5 — 150 k, ½ w
Q1, Q2 — Sylvania 2N1266 transistor	R4, R6 — 47 k, ½ w
Q3 — Sylvania 2N229 transistor	R9 — 100 Ω, ½ w
	R10 — 15 k, ½ w

Courtesy Sylvania Electric Products, Inc.

Alignment multivibrator.

The square-wave output from the emitter of Q3 is coupled through capacitor C4 to the output as a convenient signal for the troubleshooting of radios and amplifiers. When the square-wave signal is applied to the input of any stage in the radio-frequency or intermediate-frequency section of a receiver, it modulates the RF signals normally present at these points. The amplitude-modulation sidebands are subsequently detected and heard in the speaker of the set. The square-wave output signal can also be applied to the input of audio stages in receivers or high-fidelity amplifiers, producing an audible output.

GATED TURN-OFF FLIP-FLOP

A version of a flip-flop circuit using the gated turn-off switch is shown in Circuit A. The commutating capacitors C1 and C2 are connected between the anode and its complementary gate. The gated turn-off switches are General Electric type ZJ224.

Assume that switch GTO1 is conducting and switch GTO2 is triggered. Current is then taken from GTO1 through diode CR1 and resistor R1 to charge capacitor C1. This will force the gated turn-off switch 1 to turn off. After the switch is turned off, capacitor C_2 then charges to the full line voltage through resistor R4. It is ready for the next cycle when gated turn-off switch 1 is triggered. Because the charge and discharge paths for capacitors C1 and C2 are not the

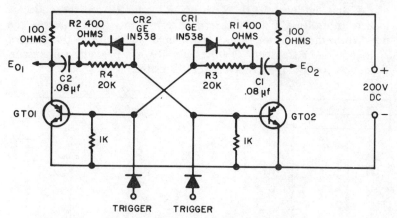

(A) Circuit using one gated turn-off switch.

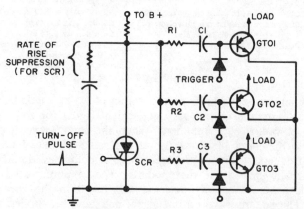

Courtesy General Electric Co.

(B) Circuit using several gated turn-off switches.

Gated-turn-off, flip-flop circuits.

same, high turn-off currents can be taken from each gate. The power source for this circuit is 200 volts DC. Circuit B shows an extension of this principle to several gated turn-off switches. This is known as a fan out array.

BISTABLE FLIP-FLOP

This circuit shows a bistable flip-flop triggered by a pulse that goes from +15 volts to +5 volts. Suppose that the TSW-60 is initially off and capacitor C2 is charged to 15 volts. Diode D1 is back biased. Under these conditions diode D2, the lower diode, is forward biased; the input pulse is coupled by capacitor C2 to the

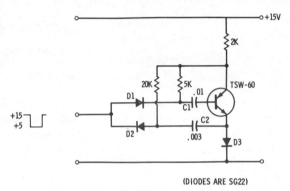

(DIODES ARE SG22)

Courtesy Transitron Electronic Corp.

Bistable flip-flop circuit.

emitter of the switch. This turns the switch on. When this happens, the collector voltage falls to about 1.5 volts, which back-biases the lower diode and creates a forward bias for diode D1. The next negative-going pulse can then be passed to the base of the TSW-60 so that it may turn the device off. In this way there are two stable states, and the device is switched from one stage to the other by the input pulse.

SHIFT REGISTER

A shift register is a series of bistable circuits. Each of these circuits feeds the next, and when properly pulsed, each stage assumes the condition of the preceding stage.

Triggering pulses are simultaneously applied to diodes D1 and D2. Note that these two shift pulses are complementary—one is positive-going and one is negative-going. If the stage originally is off, the collector voltage is at +15 volts, and D1 is reverse biased. However, D2 is forward biased, and the negative-going voltage is carried

79

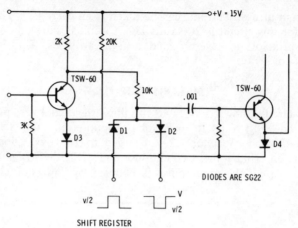

SHIFT REGISTER

DIODES ARE SG22

Courtesy Transitron Electronic Corp.

Shift-register circuit.

by the diode and the capacitor to the base of the next stage. This switches the second stage off. If, on the other hand, the first stage is on, the collector is at approximately + 1.5 volts; D2 is reverse biased and D1 is now forward biased. Thus the positive input pulse passes through the diode and the capacitor to the base of the succeeding stage, turning it on.

ONE-SHOT MULTIVIBRATOR

The one-shot, or monostable, multivibrator produces an output pulse of predetermined duration whenever a trigger pulse of sufficient amplitude is applied. In this circuit the positive trigger is applied through a coupling capacitor to the collector of transistor Q1 which is normally cut off. Transistor Q2, which is normally saturated, is now cut off by the positive pulse that is coupled through capacitor C1 to its base. The output pulse is taken from the collector of Q2. The minimum amplitude for reliable triggering depends on the value of C1, the input pulse width and the time between successive pulses. With a value of 100 mmf for C1, a 6-volt pulse is required for widths greater than 50 nanoseconds and more than 10 microseconds between successive pulses. The required amplitude increases to 17 volts as the time between pulses is reduced to 2 microseconds. For 25 nanosecond pulse widths, the minimum amplitudes are 7 and 24 volts respectively.

One-shot multivibrators are commonly used in radar circuits to generate triggers and gates. The output pulse amplitude is dependent on the source voltage, since very little voltage is dropped across Q2 when it is in saturation, and the entire source voltage is dropped

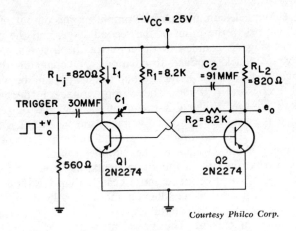

Courtesy Philco Corp.

One-shot multivibrator circuit.

across it when it is in cutoff. The upper limit of the output voltage
level is established by the reverse emitter-base voltage rating of
transistor Q2. With a value of 100 mmf for C1, a pulse width of
approximately 570 nanoseconds is obtained.

FREE-RUNNING MULTIVIBRATOR

The free-running multivibrator is essentially a nonsinusoidal two-
stage oscillator in which one stage conducts while the other is cut off.
Then the stages reverse their conditions. That is, the stage which had
been conducting cuts off, and the stage that had been cut off conducts. This oscillating process produces a square-wave output. The
free-running multivibrator circuit is a two-stage, resistance-ca-

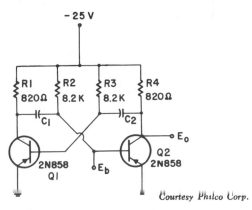

Courtesy Philco Corp.

Free-running Multivibrator circuit.

pacitance-coupled, common-emitter amplifier; the output of the first stage is coupled to the input of the second stage, and the output of the second stage is coupled to the input of the first stage. This regenerative feedback produces oscillations. By changing the values of capacitors C1 and C2, the output frequency can be varied between 1.3 cps and 1.0 mc. The output voltage is dependent on the source voltage. When Q2 is cut off, a negative output is obtained that is equal to the source voltage, and when Q2 is in saturation, the output is essentially at ground potential, resulting in a pulse ranging from ground to the supply voltage.

Because of variations in the components, one transistor conducts before the other, or it conducts more heavily than the other. Assuming that transistor Q1 is conducting more heavily than Q2, more current flows in the base circuit of Q1, resulting in a rapidly increasing collector current. The increasing voltage at the collector of Q1 is coupled through capacitor C1 to the base of Q2, decreasing the base and collector currents in Q2. The collector voltage on Q2 suddenly becomes more negative, coupling a negative voltage to the base of Q1. This action drives Q1 into saturation, and Q2 into cutoff. The action happens so quickly that capacitor C1 does not discharge, and the entire voltage increase of the collector of Q1 appears across resistor R1 and at the base of Q2. Capacitor C1 then discharges until Q2 conducts, and the cycle is completed. The resulting output from the collector of Q2 is a square wave whose amplitude is dependent on the source voltage.

SCHMITT TRIGGER

The Schmitt trigger is a flip-flop circuit that changes state when the input amplitude exceeds a certain level. Th Schmitt trigger differs from the conventional bistable multivibrator in that one of the coupling networks is replaced by a common-emitter resistor. This

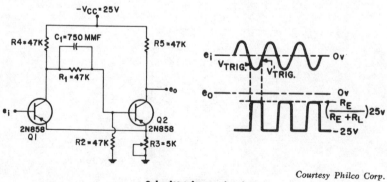

Courtesy Philco Corp.

Schmitt-trigger circuit.

arrangement provides additional regenerative feedback to obtain a faster switching time.

The emitter bias, determined by the setting of variable resistor R3, determines what level the input voltage must reach in order for the output to change state. The setting of R3 also determines the output voltage of the square wave. As R3 is varied from 0 to 5,000 ohms, the output voltage varies from approximately 24 to 9 volts, and the input voltage necessary to switch states varies from approximately 1 to 7 volts. Notice that the voltage level required to switch Q1 into conduction is lower than the voltage required to switch it to cutoff. In its quiescent condition transistor Q1 is cut off, and the collector voltage is equal to the source voltage. This voltage is coupled to the base of transistor Q2 through resistor R1, and the base voltage on Q2 is equal to the voltage drop across resistor R2. The resulting current flow through Q2 and common-emitter resistor R3 maintains the emitter of Q1 at a negative voltage. The reverse bias developed between the emitter and the base of Q1 maintains the cutoff condition. The high negative voltage at the base of Q2 produces forward bias for the base-emitter junction and causes it to operate at saturation. A negative signal of sufficient amplitude applied to the base of Q1 drives Q1 into conduction. The potential at the collector of Q1 decreases rapidly, and a positive-going voltage is coupled through capacitor C1 to the base of Q2. The emitter current of Q2 decreases, causing the voltage drop across variable resistor R3 to decrease. The emitter of Q1 becomes more positive, reducing the reverse bias and increasing the collector current. This regenerative action continues until Q1 is operating in the saturation region and Q2 is cut off. The output voltage is at maximum negative potential at this time. The new stable condition continues until the input begins to rise (become more positive). This positive-going input decreases the base potential of Q1 and increases the reverse bias. This causes the collector voltage to increase, emitter current to decrease, and the potential across resistor R3 to decrease. Simultaneously the increasing voltage at the collector of Q1 is coupled to the base of Q2, driving it negative. The decreasing voltage across R3 causes the emitter of C2 to go more positive. Both actions reduce the reverse bias of the emitter-base junction, and Q2 again operates at saturation, cutting off transistor Q1 and returning the circuit to its original operating condition; thus the cycle is completed.

A frequency divider, or counting circuit, can be made using an integrating circuit having a very long charge time compared to the period of the input wave. The voltage on the capacitor in the integrator circuit gradually builds up to a level sufficient to trigger the Schmitt-trigger circuit.

HYBRID SQUARE-WAVE MULTIVIBRATOR

The hybrid square-wave multivibrator circuit generates two out-of-phase square-wave outputs by using a trigger generated by the unijunction transistor (UJT) relaxation oscillator. The frequency of oscillation can be varied from approximately 20 cps to 600 cps by adjustment of potentiometer R3. The waveform is perfectly sym-

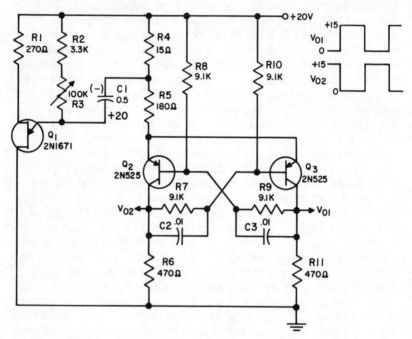

Courtesy General Electric Co.

Hybrid square-wave multivibrator circuit.

metrical over the entire frequency range. The circuit operates at temperatures as high as 75°C. Higher temperatures are possible if silicon transistors are used for Q2 and Q3. Transistors Q2 and Q3 form a simple flip-flop that is triggered by the UJT operating as a relaxation oscillator. Negative trigger pulses are generated across the 15-ohm resistor each time the UJT fires. If transformer coupling to the gates is desired, the primaries of the transformers can be connected in place of the collector resistors.

When power is applied to the circuit, transistor Q2 is conducting and Q3 is cut off. Capacitor C1 charges through resistors R2 and R3 until the capacitor voltage reaches the emitter-base 1 breakdown voltage of Q1. When Q1 fires, the emitter bias on Q2 suddenly goes negative, cutting it off. This triggers Q3 into conduction. Q2 and Q3 remain in these states until the next trigger from Q1 appears. When the next trigger is applied from Q1, Q3 cuts off and starts conducting. This action results in square-wave outputs across resistors R6 and R11, which are at the same frequency but out of phase with each other. The frequency of the output signal can be changed by adjusting R3, which controls the RC time constant of the UJT trigger circuit.

ONE-SHOT *TRIGISTOR* MULTIVIBRATOR

A one-shot multivibrator using a 3C60 *Trigistor* is shown in this circuit. It may be considered as a delayed-pulse generator that provides accurate delay times as long as 10 seconds. The output is a 1-second rectangular pulse.

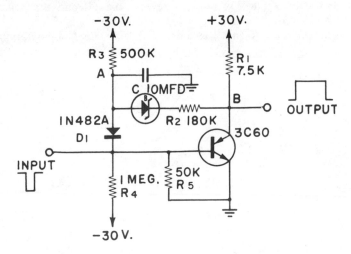

One-shot *Trigistor* multivibrator circuit.

With the circuit in its quiescent condition, the *Trigistor* is conducting, and point B is at +1 volt. At this time point A is at about −11 volts due to the voltage-divider action of R2, R3, and the 5-volt zener diode. Under these conditions diode D1 is biased in the reverse direction. A negative trigger is used as the input, and this turns the *Trigistor* off. At this time the voltage at point B rises to about +30 volts, and capacitor C begins to charge to a positive voltage through resistors R1 and R2 and the zener diode. When point A reaches about +1.5 volts, diode D1 conducts, and the *Trigistor* turns on. This brings point B back to +1 volts. Capacitor C then charges through R3 to its original voltage of −11 volts.

SHIFT REGISTER USING A *TRIGISTOR*

Circuit A shows how the *Trigistor* can be used in a memory circuit. The memory circuit provides an output pulse that is either positive or negative, depending on whether the *Trigistor* was on or off before it was pulsed. This is accomplished by means of the two diodes and capacitor C.

If the *Trigistor* was off, the capacitor charges to the supply voltage. When shift pulses are applied to points A and B with the polarities indicated, diode D2 conducts and couples a negative pulse to the output. Diode D1 stays reverse biased, hence the positive pulse is blocked. If, however, the *Trigistor* was on, the capacitor is not charged. Because of this, when the two shift pulses are applied to A and B, diode D1 conducts and couples the positive pulse to the output. However, diode D2 remains reverse biased, and the negative pulse is blocked.

Because circuit A can "remember" the last state of operation, it

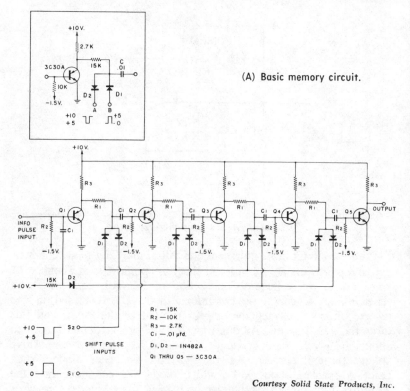

(A) Basic memory circuit.

Courtesy Solid State Products, Inc.

(B) Five-bit shift register.

Trigistor shift-register circuit.

can be used as a one-bit memory circuit that may be connected in cascade to form a complete shift register. Circuit B shows a complete shift register with two shift-pulse inputs and a single information-pulse input. For every pair of shift pulses, the state of the shift register changes by one pulse at a time, and the unit that was on turns off in the sequence necessary to form the shift register.

OTHER SWITCHING CIRCUITS

PROXIMITY SWITCH

This circuit uses the silicon-controlled rectifier as a proximity switch. The AC voltage input, which can be 115 volts from the power line, is essentially across C1 and C2 in series. C1 is variable, while C2 is the capacitance of the sensor plate to ground. As shown in the schematic, the sensor plate is 6 inches square by 1/16 inch thick, but the size can be varied, as mentioned later. The AC voltage present across capacitor C1 depends on the voltage divider network and the line voltage, which can be differ-

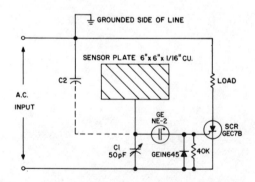

NOTES: (1) C2 IS EQUIVALENT CAPACITY OF SENSOR PLATE W.R.T. GROUND.
(2) SENSOR PLATE AREA MAY BE ADJUSTED FOR REQUIRED SENSITIVITY.

Courtesy General Electric Co.

Proximity switch circuit.

ent from 117 volts, if it is required. The equivalent capacity of C2 depends on the area of the sensor plate and its proximity to a grounded object such as metal or the human body.

As soon as the voltage across C1 is greater than the breakover potential of the neon lamp, capacitors C1 and C2 discharge through the SCR gate. This causes the controlled rectifier to trigger and energize the load, which can be a relay, motor, or alarm, depending on the circuit. It is also possible to obtain latching action by using direct current for the anode circuit supply only. The sensitivity of this circuit depends on the sensing distance and the plate that is used for the sensor. It is possible to make the sensing plate as small as 1 inch in diameter if it is used for a touch control. A sensor such as this can be used for controlling elevators, safety doors, supermarket doors, conveyor-belt counting systems, or other similar applications.

PHASE-SENSITIVE SWITCHING CIRCUIT

Circuit A shows a phase-sensitive switch using an SCR. Transformer T1 is a 6.3-volt filament transformer. The primary is connected across the 115-volt AC input, and the secondary is connected as part of the bridge circuit. T2 is a transformer with a center-tapped secondary. This transformer has a one-to-one turns ratio.

When the bridge is balanced, the AC output is 0, and there is no input to the gate of the controlled rectifier. This bridge is, of course, temperature-sensitive since the thermistor is a temperature-sensitive resistor. When the bridge is unbalanced by a change in temperature, there will be an AC voltage appearing across the terminals marked AB. This voltage is applied to the gate of the SCR. When this voltage has one polarity, the controlled rectifier turns on, and there is current flow through load 1, while diode CR2 blocks the current to load 2. If, however, the voltage has the opposite polarity, diode CR2 conducts so that power is delivered to load 2 while CR1 is reverse-biased. Diode CR3 is used to prevent excessive negative voltage from appearing across the controlled rectifier. The polarity depends on whether the resistance of the thermistor increases or decreases; this in turn depends on the change in temperature.

With the values used in this circuit, there is a response to changes in temperature of about 1 to 2°C, and this system can be used for temperature monitoring. Because there is a dual-load output, one load can be a high-temperature indicator and the other can be a low-temperature indicator. Illustration B shows a circuit for a temperature-sensitive switch designed for use with a single-ended load

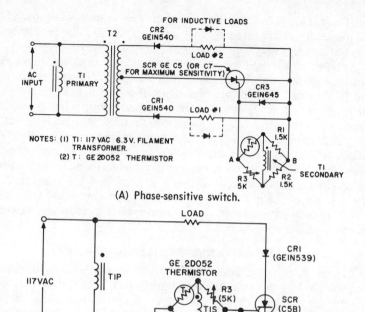

(A) Phase-sensitive switch.

(B) Temperature-sensitive switch.
Phase-sensitive switching circuit.

Courtesy *General Electric Co.*

TEMPERATURE-CONTROLLED SWITCHING

Thermistors can be used to drive a controlled switch (CS) directly with simple circuits. Consider circuit A using a power source of 200 volts (AC or DC) and a load of up to 200 watts.

The gate of the CS is tied to the zero-potential junction of the thermistor R_A and reference resistor R_B. When resistance R_A becomes smaller than R_B, providing positive gate current, the CS triggers on. Thus the CS turns on when the thermistor temperature rises above the set value. If the thermistor and reference resistor are interchanged, the CS will operate when the thermistor temperature falls.

Anode-supply voltage for the CS can be either AC or DC, providing for two entirely different modes of operation. With a DC anode supply, after the CS is triggered on, it remains in this state until deliberately reset by momentarily interrupting the anode current. This mode of operation of the CS makes it useful as a temperature-limit switch with latching action.

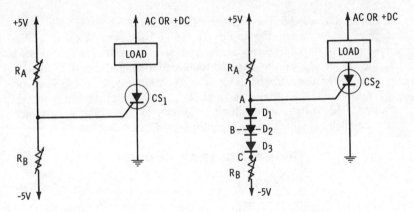

R$_A$, R$_B$ - Thermistor and ref. resistor . . . approx. 2K at temp. set point.

CS$_1$ - 2N876 or 2N 1869 (3A15A) series . (gate trigger current 200 μA max.)

CS$_2$ - 2N884 or 2N 1875 (3A16) series. (gate trigger current 20 μA max.)

D$_1$, D$_2$, D$_3$ - Germanium diode - 1N118A

Courtesy Solid State Products, Inc.

(A) Uncompensated circuit.   (B) Temperature-compensated circuit.

Temperature-controlled switching circuits.

With AC anode supply voltage, the CS turns on and off auto-matically as the thermistor temperature changes above and below the set point. Each negative half-cycle of the AC supply voltage resets the CS, which does not turn on again during successive positive half-cycles unless a positive gate trigger signal is sustained. In this mode of operation the CS not only controls, but also rectifies the power applied to the load. DC relays or sole-noids should be used even though the supply voltage is AC. With inductive loads a shunt diode enables the load current to "free-wheel" during the negative half-cycle of AC supply voltage.

This circuit is not compensated for variations in CS gate-trigger voltage resulting from changes in junction temperature. Tempera-ture-sensing error is approximately 5°C for an ambient tempera-ture change from −65°C to +125°C, or about 0.5°C for a 20°C change in ambient temperature. Circuit B reduces this temperature-sensing error to less than 0.5°C over an ambient-temperature range of −65°C to + 125°C.

There are three germanium diodes in the input circuit to com-pensate for CS gate-trigger voltage changes due to temperature. When R$_A$ is exactly equal to R$_B$, zero potential exists at B. At 25°C the voltage drop across the three germanium diodes is approximately 1.0 volt (A is at + 0.5 volt and B is at − .05 volt). Since the CS gate-trigger voltage is also approximately + 0.5 volt at 25°C, the diodes provide an offset voltage equal to the gate-trigger voltage when the input circuit is balanced. With B as an imaginary null point there are effectively one and one-half diodes in the upper leg of the input circuit and one and one-half diodes in the lower leg. Each diode has a temperature coefficient of -2 millivolts/°C so that if R_A and R_B are equal but the temperature changes, the voltage at A changes exactly as the CS-gate temperature coefficient, which is -3 millivolts/°C.

HIGH-SPEED RELAY CONTROL

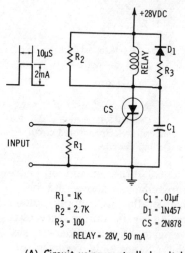

R₁ = 1K   C₁ = .01μf
R₂ = 2.7K   D₁ = 1N457
R₃ = 100   CS = 2N878
RELAY = 28V, 50 mA

(A) Circuit using controlled switch.

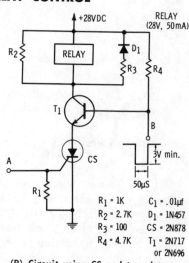

R₁ = 1K   C₁ = .01μf
R₂ = 2.7K   D₁ = 1N457
R₃ = 100   CS = 2N878
R₄ = 4.7K   T₁ = 2N717
                  or 2N696

(B) Circuit using CS and transistor.

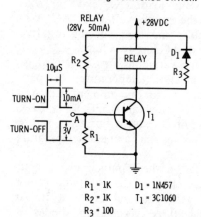

(C) Circuit using 3C1060 transistor.

R₁ = 1K   D₁ = 1N457
R₂ = 1K   T₁ = 3C1060
R₃ = 100

Courtesy Solid State Products, Inc.

High-speed relay control circuits.

In some industrial applications relays are to be controlled by short-duration, low-level pulses. In these applications regular latching relays are not satisfactory.

In circuit A the 28-volt, 50-milliampere relay is normally off. An input pulse or trigger turns the controlled switch (SCR) on. Resistor R2 allows the current to rise above the holding level while the pulse is present; hence, when the pulse is no longer present, the switch remains on and full voltage is across the relay. The time required for the relay to energize is not important from a circuit viewpoint. This circuit is reset by momentarily interrupting the anode current.

Circuit B shows a 2N717 transistor used in series with the 2N878 controlled switch (CS). Resistor R4 provides saturating base drive to the transistor. To reset the circuit a negative pulse is applied to the transistor base. This momentarily interrupts the anode current of the CS, and the CS turns off. The CS remains off until a turn-on command pulse is applied at A.

Circuit C uses a silicon *Trigistor* (PNPN switch) as the active control element. Since the *Trigistor* can be turned off as well as on at its base terminal, it can perform the same function Circuit B, but with fewer components. Command pulses for both turn-on and turn-off are applied at point A. Turn-off time can be significantly shorter with the *Trigistor* approach.

SIMPLE ON-OFF SWITCH

The on-off switch is perhaps the most simple circuit that uses controlled rectifiers. The controlled rectifier is the solid-state equiv-

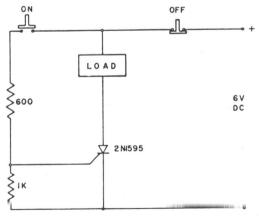

Courtesy Transitron Electronic Corp.

Circuit of simple on-off switch.

alent of the thyratron for use in many types of control circuits. The fast switching times and extreme triggering sensitivities of the controlled rectifier make it suitable for use in pulse and digital circuits wherever high voltages and currents are needed.

When the on switch is depressed, a current of about 10 ma flows into the gate of the controlled rectifier, switching it on. Once the controlled rectifier has been gated on, the gate current is no longer required to hold it on. When the off switch is depressed, the controlled rectifier is switched off. When the off switch is released, the anode voltage is again applied, but the TCR remains off. If this circuit is used for switching a high voltage or at a high temperature, the internal capacitance together with a fast anode voltage rise time in the Off state can provide enough current to the gate so that the TCR switches on without having external gate current. This can be avoided by adding an RC network in the anode circuit to slow down the rate of rise of the anode voltage. The load current can be anywhere between the rated current and the holding current of the TCR.

TRANSISTOR AUTOMOBILE IGNITION 1

This circuit shows the use of a 2N2527 transistor in an automotive ignition system. In the conventional ignition system, gears from the crankshaft drive a cam to open and close the breaker points. Primary current builds up to a maximum value when the points are closed; when the points open, the collapse of the magnetic field induces a high voltage across the secondary. Using the transistor in the circuit as shown allows the points to carry only

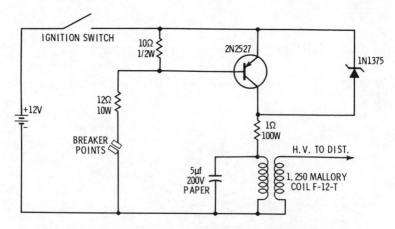

Courtesy Motorola Semiconductor Products, Inc.
Transistor automobile-ignition circuit.

a fraction of the total current, thus increasing their life expectancy and reducing maintenance. As shown, a zener diode is used to prevent a voltage surge from damaging the transistor. This diode conducts only when the collector-to-emitter voltage across the transistor approaches the maximum rating.

TRANSISTOR AUTOMOBILE IGNITION 2

The basic PNPN pulse modulator circuit makes an excellent high-performance electronic ignition system for automobiles. Addition of a light-activated switch (LAS) to the original circuit also allows the troublesome breaker points to be eliminated.

The 12-volt auto supply is converted to approximately 150 volts DC with a low-cost, germanium-transistor converter. With power applied, capacitor C1 charges to twice the supply voltage through the charging action of inductor L1 and diode CR1. A rotating disc, as shown, driven by the engine distributor is punched to correspond to the number of engine cylinders and the desired tim-

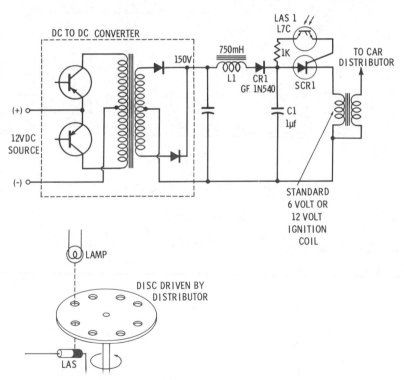

Courtesy General Electric Co.

Automobile-ignition circuit.

ing angle. Each time a hole in the disc passes the light source, light-activated switch LAS1 is switched on. When LAS1 is switched on, a bias voltage is applied to the gate of controlled rectifier SCR1, switching it on. When SCR1 is switched on, capacitor C1 discharges through the primary winding of T1. The high-voltage, induced secondary pulse that results is transmitted to the engine spark plugs in the normal manner. Resonant action between C1 and T1 turns off SCR1 in readiness for the next pulse. This circuit is capable of putting out 20- to 25-kilovolt pulses with no decrease in magnitude up to 8,200 rpm with a 6- or 8-cylinder engine.

FULL RANGE UJT PHASE CONTROL

This circuit is a simple and low-cost phase-control circuit employing a unijunction transistor to trigger a controlled rectifier. Through the use of a power diode and a switch, the circuit provides nonsymmetrical, continuously variable AC phase-shift control

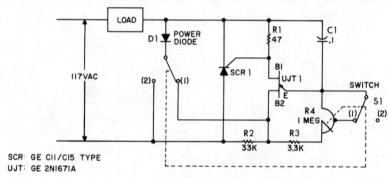

Courtesy General Electric Co.

Full-range UJT phase-control circuit.

over the load voltage from zero to 100%.

When variable resistor R4 is set in the bottom portion of the resistor range, switch S1 is in position (1) and power diode D1 is connected to the base 2 circuit of unijunction transistor UJT1. The circuit now provides only half-wave phase control to the load. UJT1 is essentially a ratio device; when its emitter-base 1 voltage reaches the fraction (usually 50 to 70%) of the base 2-base 1 (interbase) voltage, its emitter-base 1 diode switches into a low-impedance state. Capacitor C1 is charged through resistors R2, R3, and the bottom half of R4 (the top half is shorted by switch S1). When its voltage reaches the level necessary to trigger UJT1, C1 discharges through UJT1 and resistor R1, producing a pulse at the gate of controlled rectifier SCR1, triggering SCR1 on.

Dropping resistor R2 supplies both the UJT interbase and the variable RC emitter-timing circuits. Controlled rectifier SCR1 continues to conduct, allowing current to pass through the load until the end of the half cycle at which time its anode voltage goes negative and switches it off. The setting of variable resistor R4 determines the charge time of C1, therefore controlling the phase angle at which SCR1 fires. When R4 is rotated to the upper portion of the resistance range, switch S1 is placed in position (2) and power diode D1 is placed in series with the load. Now capacitor C1 charges through resistors R2, R3, and the top portion of R4 (the bottom portion is shorted by the wiper arm) and discharges through the same path as before. Therefore, when R4 is set in the upper portion of the resistor, the circuit is a full-wave phase control, and when R4 is set in the lower portion of the resistor, the circuit is a half-wave phase control. This results in phase control over load voltage from zero to 100%.

FULL-WAVE SCR-BRIDGE PHASE CONTROL

This circuit provides a very smooth operating, full-wave, phase-controlled circuit with excellent symmetry of the output waveform. It employs a gated-diode bridge using a unijunction transistor to gate a controlled rectifier. The full-wave circuit gives full symmetrical control over load voltage from zero to 100%. The use of power diodes provides a cheaper method of full-wave phase control than could be obtained with two controlled rectifiers connected back to back.

During the positive half-cycle (when the voltage at the anode of power diode CR1 is positive), a charging current flows through power

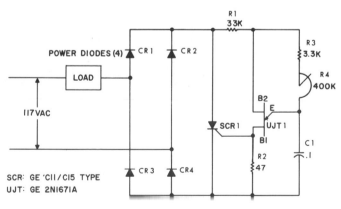

Courtesy General Electric Co.

Circuit for full-wave SCR-bridge phase control.

diode CR4, capacitor C1, resistors R4, R3, R1, and power diode CR1. This current charges C1 until it reaches the proper voltage to gate unijunction transistor UJT1 into conduction. (UJT1 is essentially a ratio device; when its emitter-base 1 voltage reaches the fraction n, usually 50 to 70%, of the interbase voltage, its emitter-base 1 diode switches into a low-impedance state.)

When UJT1 conducts, capacitor C1 discharges through UJT1 and resistor R2, producing a gating pulse at the gate of controlled rectifier SCR1. This gating pulse triggers SCR1 on, and current flows through CR4, SCR1, CR1, and the load until the end of the positive half-cycle. At the end of the positive half-cycle the voltage across SCR1 drops to zero, and it stops conducting. During the negative half-cycle (when the voltage at the anode of CR1 is negative), a charging current flows through power diode CR3, capacitor C1, resistors R4, R3, R1, and power diode CR4. Capacitor C1 again charges until UJT1 is biased into conduction, gating SCR1 on. Current flows through the load for the remainder of the negative half-cycle. Since the charge time of C1 is dependent on the value of C1 and the combined resistance of the load and resistors R1, R3, and R4, adjustment of R4 controls the triggering time of SCR1 and controls the current allowed to pass through the load.

FULL-WAVE CROSS-COUPLED UNIJUNCTION TRANSISTOR PHASE CONTROL

This circuit is especially well suited for manual control where four power diodes cannot be tolerated and a transformerless trigger circuit of minimum heat dissipation is required. The circuit employs two

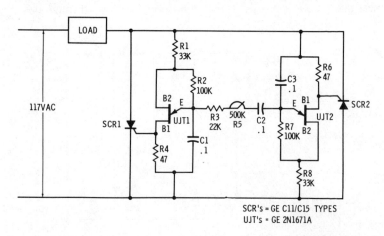

SCR's = GE C11/C15 TYPES
UJT's = GE 2N1671A

Courtesy General Electric Co.

Circuit for full-wave, cross-coupled, unijunction-transistor phase control.

parallel-inverse controlled rectifiers (SCR's) as the full-wave circuit. Each SCR, however, has its own associated unijunction-transistor (UJT) trigger circuit.

Control is achieved by AC cross-coupling the two timing circuits with an RC network containing the control potentiometer. During the positive half-cycle (when the voltage at the anode of controlled rectifier SCR1 is positive), capacitor C1 starts to charge through resistors R2 and R1 and the load. However, some of the charge on C1 flows into capacitor C2 through resistors R3 and R5. Therefore, the charge time of C1 is dependent not only on the resistance of R1 and R2, but also on the current in the branch containing C2. Therefore the setting of variable resistor R5 determines the charge time of C1. C1 charges until it reaches the proper emitter-base 1 voltage of unijunction transistor UJT1 to gate it into conduction. Capacitor C1 now discharges through UJT1 and R4, producing a gating pulse at the gate of controlled rectifier SCR1. This gating pulse triggers SCR1 on, and current flows through the load for the remainder of the positive half-cycle.

At the end of the positive half-cycle the voltage across SCR1 drops to zero, and SCR1 stops conducting. During the negative half-cycle (that is, when the voltage at the anode of SCR2 becomes positive), capacitor C3 charges through resistors R7 and R8 and the load. Again some of the charge flows into C2, and the charge time of C3 is determined by the setting of R5. C3 charges until it reaches the proper emitter-base 1 voltage of UJT2 to gate it into conduction, discharging itself through UJT2 and R6. This, in turn, gates SCR2 on, and current flows through the load for the remainder of the negative half-cycle, thus completing the cycle.

FULL-WAVE SINGLE-UNIJUNCTION TRANSISTOR PHASE CONTROL

This transformerless trigger circuit uses only one unijunction transistor (UJT) to operate two parallel-inverse connected controlled rectifiers (SCR's). It uses two steering diodes (CR1 and CR2) to supply positive half-cycles to the single unijunction transistor (UJT1). A suitable network, consisting of resistors R3 and R4 and capacitors C3 and C4, provides the necessary return circuit.

During the positive half-cycle (that is, when the anode voltage on SCR1 is positive), a charging current flows through capacitors C4 and C5, resistors R6, R5, diode CR1, and the load. When the charge on C5 reaches the proper emitter-base 1 voltage on UJT1, it discharges through UJT1 and resistor R8, producing a positive pulse at the base 1 of UJT1. The charge time of C5 is controlled by variable resistor R6. The pulse from the base of UJT1 is coupled to the gates of controlled rectifiers SCR1 and SCR2. Since the voltage at the anode of

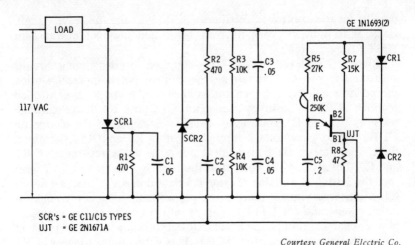

Courtesy General Electric Co.

Circuit for full-wave, single-unijunction, transistor phase control.

SCR1 is positive, SCR1 is now switched on and continues conducting until the end of the positive half-cycle, at which time the voltage across SCR1 drops to zero and it ceases to conduct.

During the negative half-cycle (that is, when the voltage at the cathode of SCR1 is positive), a charging current flows through capacitors C3 and C5, resistors R6, R5, and diode CR2. Capacitor C5 again charges until UJT1 is triggered and then discharges, producing a positive pulse at the gate of SCR2. SCR2 now conducts for the remainder of the negative half-cycle, thus completing the cycle. Therefore the setting of R6 determines the charge time for C5 during both positive and negative half-cycles and in turn determines the firing time of UJT1, which controls the firing time of SCR1 and SCR2.

SCR LATCHING RELAY

By combining the characteristics of square-loop core materials with the silicon-controlled rectifier (SCR) many useful circuits can be developed. This circuit uses two small toroidal cores in conjunction with two back-to-back SCR's to secure a direct analogy to a single-pole electromechanical contactor with an electrically isolated solenoid. With slight modification, an analogy to an electromechanical latching relay results.

When gate signals are applied to SCR1 and SCR2, they conduct and supply full-wave AC to the load, thus simulating the closed contacts of a relay or contactor. If no gate signal is applied to the SCR's, the switch is open. During the open state cores T1 and T2 are saturated by the flow of current from the main AC supply through their

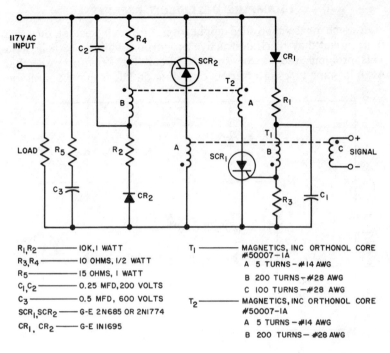

R_1, R_2	10K, 1 WATT	T_1	MAGNETICS, INC ORTHONOL CORE #50007-1A
R_3, R_4	10 OHMS, 1/2 WATT		A 5 TURNS -#14 AWG
R_5	15 OHMS, 1 WATT		B 200 TURNS -#28 AWG
C_1, C_2	0.25 MFD, 200 VOLTS		C 100 TURNS -#28 AWG
C_3	0.5 MFD, 600 VOLTS	T_2	MAGNETICS, INC ORTHONOL CORE #50007-1A
SCR_1, SCR_2	G-E 2N685 OR 2N1774		A 5 TURNS -#14 AWG
CR_1, CR_2	G-E 1N1695		B 200 TURNS- #28 AWG

Courtesy General Electric Co.

SCR-latching—relay circuit.

respective B windings during alternate halves of the cycle. This current is limited by resistors R1 and R2 respectively. Under these conditions, the gate voltage applied to the SCR's is limited to less than 0.25 volt by the voltage-dividing action of R1 and R3 across SCR1 and R2 and R4 across SCR2. Neither SCR fires, and no current flows in any of the reset windings of the cores. If a low-level voltage is now applied to the signal (C) winding of T1, this core will reset during the half cycle that the anode of SCR1 is negative and CR1 is blocking.

When the anode of SCR1 starts to swing positive on the following half cycle, winding B on T1 sustains part of the supply voltage, and capacitor C1 charges through CR1 and R1. After about 1 or 2 milliseconds the core of T1 is saturated, and C1 discharges through the gate of SCR1, firing it. Current will now flow through the load and SCR1 for the remainder of the half cycle. The gate-firing circuit of SCR2 is identical to that of SCR1 except that no separate signal winding is used. Core T2 depends on current through its A winding to reset the core and thus permit firing of SCR2. SCR2 fires on the following half cycle, and full-wave voltage is applied to the load.

16-AMPERE DC CIRCUIT BREAKER

In some phase-controlled applications the fault current due to a short circuit may reach destructive proportions within one-half cycle. This prohibits use of conventional circuit breakers for protection. Also, in some types of inverters operating on DC it may be desirable

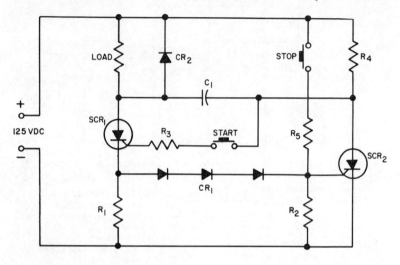

$R_1 \cong 3/I_{trip}$ OHMS NON-INDUCTIVE

R_2—220 OHMS, 1/2 WATT

R_3—100 OHMS, 1/2 WATT

R_4—2200 OHMS, 10 WATTS

R_5—2200 OHMS, 5 WATTS

$C_1 \cong 0.4 I_{trip}$ MFD

SCR_1, SCR_2 - G.E. C40B

CR_1 - (3) G.E. IN1692

CR_2 - G.E. IN2158

Courtesy General Electric Co.

Schematic of 16-ampere DC circuit breaker.

to have a fast electronic circuit breaker in the event of loss of commutation in the inverter for any reason. This circuit provides these protective functions very nicely.

The circuit breaker is essentially a parallel capacitor-commutated flip-flop. When the start button is depressed, a positive voltage is applied to the gate of controlled rectifier (SCR1), switching it on. Current is now allowed to pass through the load, SCR1, and resistor R1. Capacitor C1 charges through resistor R4 to the voltage across the load. When the stop button is depressed, a positive voltage is applied to the gate of SCR2, switching it on. Capacitor C1 is now essentially connected across SCR1, and the positive charge on the right-hand plate of C1 reverse-biases SCR1 into the Off state. When SCR1 is on, the circuit may also be shut off if the voltage drop across R1 be-

102

comes large enough to cause series-connected diodes CR1 to conduct. When this occurs, current flows through R2 and CR1, developing a positive voltage at the gate of SCR2, switching it on. Again, when SCR2 switches on, capacitor C1 reverse-biases SCR1, switching it off. By adjusting the value of R1 and by selecting the proper number of series diodes, the circuit can be made to trip out and interrupt overload or fault current at any predetermined level.

SCR CIRCUIT BREAKER

This circuit provides the same protective functions as the previous one plus a circuit for tripping the breaker as soon as the start button is depressed, if there is a short across the load.

The circuit breaker is essentially a parallel capacitor-commutated flip-flop. When the start button is depressed, a positive voltage is applied to the gate of controlled rectifier SCR1, switching it on. Current is now allowed to pass through the load, SCR1, and resistor R1. If,

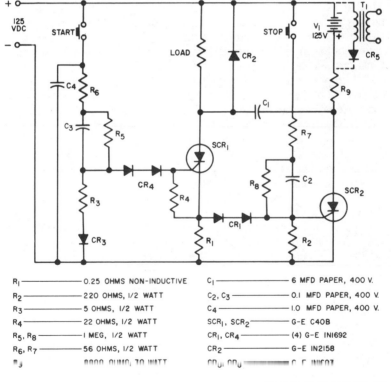

R$_1$	0.25 OHMS NON-INDUCTIVE	C$_1$	6 MFD PAPER, 400 V.
R$_2$	220 OHMS, 1/2 WATT	C$_2$, C$_3$	0.1 MFD PAPER, 400 V.
R$_3$	5 OHMS, 1/2 WATT	C$_4$	1.0 MFD PAPER, 400 V.
R$_4$	22 OHMS, 1/2 WATT	SCR$_1$, SCR$_2$	G-E C40B
R$_5$, R$_8$	1 MEG, 1/2 WATT	CR$_1$, CR$_4$	(4) G-E 1N1692
R$_6$, R$_7$	56 OHMS, 1/2 WATT	CR$_2$	G-E 1N2158
R$_9$	8000 OHMS, 70 WATT	CR$_3$, CR$_5$	G-E 1N1692

Courtesy General Electric Co.

SCR circuit-breaker schematic.

when SCR1 is turned on by the start button, normal load current flows, the circuit will continue to operate.

If, on the other hand, a short circuit exists in the load, the current through R1 will increase rapidly until the voltage across R1 exceeds the forward breakdown voltage of CR1. At this point, current flows through R2 and CR1, developing a positive voltage at the gate of SCR2. SCR2 now conducts, and capacitor C1, which was previously charged through an independent power supply of approximately the same voltage as the source, is placed across SCR1. The positive charge on C1 is applied to the cathode of SCR1, switching it off immediately. As long as the fault exists, it will be impossible to keep the circuit turned on. When the stop button is depressed, a positive voltage is applied to the gate of SCR2, switching it on. Charge capacitor C1 is again placed across SCR1, switching it off.

CIRCUIT BREAKER WITH AUTOMATIC RECLOSING

In some phase-controlled applications the fault current due to a short circuit may reach destructive proportions within one-half cycle. This would prohibit use of conventional circuit breakers for protection. Also, in some types of inverters operating on DC it may be desirable to have a fast electronic circuit breaker in the event of loss of commutation in the inverter for any reason. This circuit features these functions and an automatic reclosing circuit.

Before power is applied to the load, capacitor C1 is charged through diode CR2 and resistor R7. A seperate power supply of approximately the same voltage as the source is used to charge C1. When start-stop switch S1 is closed, capacitor C2 charges through resistor R4 to the emitter-base 1 breakdown voltage of unijunction transistor Q1. When the charge on C2 reaches this level, Q1 is triggered on and C2 discharges through resistor R3, producing a positive pulse at the gate of controlled rectifier SCR1. SCR1 now conducts. If the load is short-circuited, the current through resistor R1 increases to the point where the voltage drop across R1 is greater than the forword breakdown voltage of diode CR1. Current now flows through resistor R2 and CR1, producing a positive voltage at the gate of controlled rectifier SCR2. SCR2 now conducts, and previously charged capacitor C1 is effectively placed across SCR1. Since the right side of C1 is positively charged, SCR1 will be back biased and switched off. As long as the fault exists, it will be impossible to keep the circuit turned on. If, when S1 is closed, normal load current flows, the circuit continues to conduct since the voltage drop across R1 does not exceed the forward breakdown voltage of CR1. If at any time there should be a temporary short, the circuit will shut off as previously mentioned. However, when the short disappears, the switching action of Q1 recloses the circuit, and current again flows through the load.

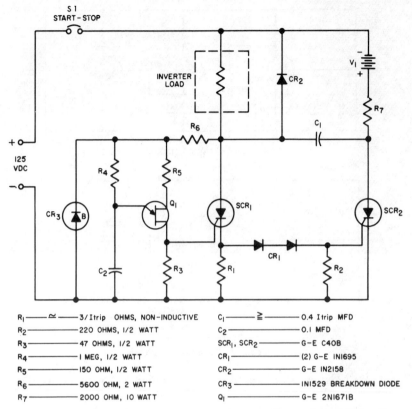

R_1	$\approx$	3/Itrip OHMS, NON-INDUCTIVE	C_1	$\geqq$	0.4 Itrip MFD
R_2		220 OHMS, 1/2 WATT	C_2		0.1 MFD
R_3		47 OHMS, 1/2 WATT	SCR_1, SCR_2		G-E C40B
R_4		1 MEG, 1/2 WATT	CR_1		(2) G-E 1N1695
R_5		150 OHM, 1/2 WATT	CR_2		G-E 1N2158
R_6		5600 OHM, 2 WATT	CR_3		1N1529 BREAKDOWN DIODE
R_7		2000 OHM, 10 WATT	Q_1		G-E 2N1671B

Courtesy General Electric Co.

Schematic of circuit breaker with automatic reclosing.

HIGH-CURRENT SWITCH

Two possible variations for high-current, solid-state switches are shown. In each case load current from 1 to 15 amperes can be switched using these circuits to replace relays. These switches are designed for normally off operation in which the load can be switched on in either of two ways. The load can be switched on by activating normally closed switch S1, or the load can be switched on by applying a small input signal which exceeds a certain threshold. The load is turned off either by closing switch S1 or by reducing the input below the threshold. For the circuits shown, the current through switch S1 is 15 ma. For switching with an input signal instead of S1, a 3-volt DC source capable of supplying about 40 milliwatts is necessary.

Circuit A is a 15-ampere switch with a load resistance of 1.53 ohms. The output power is 343 watts at 15 amperes with an efficiency

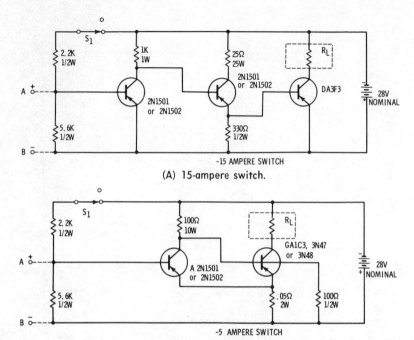

(A) 15-ampere switch.

(B) 5-ampere switch.

Courtesy Minneapolis-Honeywell Regulator Co.

Circuit for high-current switch.

of 82%. The output power in the off condition is 1.1 milliwatts. The input signal required for turn-on is 3 volts.

Circuit B is a 5-ampere switch with a 4.86-ohm load resistance. The output power in the on condition is 134 watts at 5.25 amperes with an efficiency of 90%. The output power in the off condition is 3.0 milliwatts, and the input signal required for turn on is 3 volts.

TRANSISTORIZED IGNITION SYSTEM

Transistorized ignition systems where the current flow passing through the points is substantially reduced through the use of a transistor have two major advantages over normal types of ignition systems. First, there is less wear on the breaker points since the breaker points carry less current, and there is very little, if any, high voltage fall-off at high engine speeds. The use of a transistorized system, of course, increases the reliability and life expectancy of this type of ignition arrangement.

The transistors that are used should have four important characteristics for this application. The input impedance should be low because there is a limited amount of energy for the switch core. The

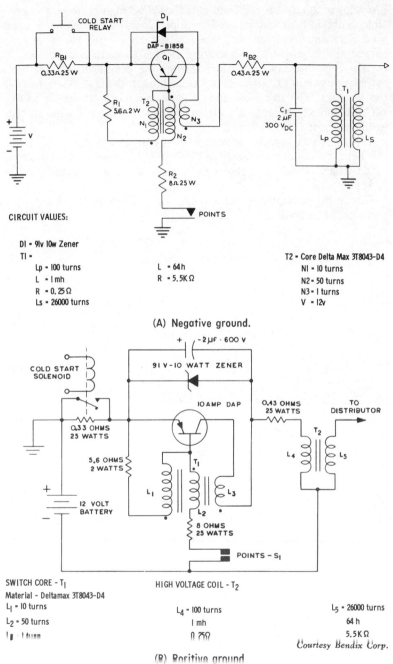

CIRCUIT VALUES:

DI = 9lv 10w Zener
TI =
    Lp = 100 turns
    L = 1 mh   L = 64h
    R = 0.25Ω   R = 5.5KΩ
    Ls = 26000 turns

T2 = Core Delta Max 3T8043-D4
    NI = 10 turns
    N2 = 50 turns
    N3 = 1 turns
    V = 12v

(A) Negative ground.

SWITCH CORE - T_1
Material - Deltamax 3T8043-D4
L_1 = 10 turns
L_2 = 50 turns
L_3 = 1 turn

HIGH VOLTAGE COIL - T_2

L_4 = 100 turns
    1 mh
    0.25Ω

L_5 = 26000 turns
    64 h
    5.5KΩ

Courtesy Bendix Corp.

(B) Positive ground.

Transistorized ignition-system circuits.

breakdown voltage for the transistor should be high because it is possible to obtain high voltages under various conditions, such as an open secondary or problems with the voltage regulator. The transistor should also be capable of operating at high temperatures because in certain situations, such as when starting the engine, there will be a sufficient amount of power dissipation through the transistors to heat the junction. The transistor should also be able to be driven to the off state quickly because it is desired to turn off the collector current in the shortest possible time.

Circuit A is a negative-ground system designed for 12 volts, using the Bendix 10-ampere transistor DAP-B-1858 together with a zener diode which is used to protect the transistor from transient voltage spikes.

Circuit B is a positive ground system with the necessary changes for this type of operation.

PHOTOELECTRIC DEVICES

DIFFERENTIAL PHOTO RELAY

The differential photo-relay circuit requires two photocells, and the circuit responds to a difference in light between these two cells. This is somewhat like a bridge circuit in which the operation depends on the unbalance between the two elements. As shown, there are two photocells whose resistance is a function of the light falling on them. These two photocells are connected in series across the 12-volt source, and their mid-point is tied to the base of transistor Q1. In operation either photocell decreases in resistance and then the other decreases in resistance. The sequence depends on how an object passes by the two photocells and affects the light falling on them.

An object passing the photo cells will cause a negative-going pulse and then a positive-going pulse to appear at the base of Q1, or the sequence can be reversed. In either case the pulse is amplified by Q2, and through capacitor C3 the amplified pulse is applied to the trigger circuit made up of transistors Q3 and Q4. The trigger circuit converts the signal created by the photocells and amplified by the first two stages into a sharp pulse which can be either positive or negative, depending on the setting of control R6. The pulse output from the trigger circuit is used to control a multivibrator composed of transistors Q5 and Q6. The output of the multivibrator, in turn, operates the relay. The length of time the relay remains closed depends on the value of capacitor C5. This relay is closed whenever the object passing the two photocells causes a trigger-circuit output. R6 controls the sensitivity of the circuit and requires adjustment according to specific circumstances.

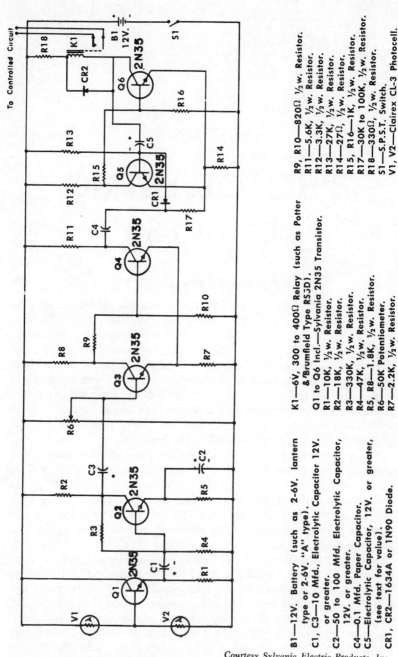

B1—12V. Battery (such as 2-6V. lantern type or 2-6V. "A" type).

C1, C3—10 Mfd., Electrolytic Capacitor 12V. or greater.

C2—50 to 100 Mfd. Electrolytic Capacitor, 12V. or greater.

C4—0.1 Mfd. Paper Capacitor.

C5—Electrolytic Capacitor, 12V. or greater, (see text for value).

CR1, CR2—1634A or 1N90 Diode.

K1—6V, 300 to 400Ω Relay (such as Potter &/Brumfield Type RS5D).

Q1 to Q6 Incl.—Sylvania 2N35 Transistor.

R1—10K, ½w. Resistor.
R2—18K, ½w. Resistor.
R3—330K, ½w. Resistor.
R4—47K, ½w. Resistor.
R5, R8—1.8K, ½w. Resistor.
R6—50K Potentiometer.
R7—2.2K, ½w. Resistor.

R9, R10—820Ω ½w. Resistor.
R11—5.6K, ½w. Resistor.
R12—3.3K, ½w. Resistor.
R13—27K, ½w. Resistor.
R14—27Ω, ½w. Resistor.
R15, R16—1K, ½w. Resistor.
R17—30K to 100K, ½w. Resistor.
R18—330Ω, ½w. Resistor.
S1—S.P.S.T. Switch.
V1, V2—Clairex CL-3 Photocell.

Courtesy Sylvania Electric Products, Inc.

Differential photo-relay circuit.

110

PHOTO-RELAY CIRCUIT

This circuit shows a sensitive three-transistor photo-relay circuit using a photoresistive cell. The relay is operated when the light intensity falls below a predetermined level. The operating point is determined by the setting of R1. The range of adjustment is such that the relay is energized in bright light and held open when it is dark. The maximum power controlled by this relay depends on the relay contacts themselves. Two amperes can be accommodated in the circuit at 115 volts with this particular relay.

The photosensitive element is V1. Variations of light intensity on this photocell vary its resistance. Q1 is an emitter follower with a high-impedance input; this circuit drives Q2. Note that a bias battery is

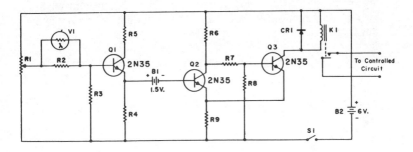

B1—1 to 1.5V. Battery (such as penlite or small mercury cell).
B2—6V. Battery (such as lantern type or "A" type).
CR1—1N34 Diode.
K1—6V., 300Ω or greater Relay (such as Potter & Brumfield Type RS5D).
Q1, Q2, Q3—Sylvania 2N35 Transistor.
R1—10K Potentiometer.

R2, R3—100K, ½w. Resistor.
R4—4.7 to 5.6K, ½w. Resistor.
R5—200Ω to 1K, ½w. Resistor.
R6—1.2K, ½w. Resistor.
R7, R8—3.3K, ½w. Resistor.
R9—27Ω, ½w. Resistor.
S1—S.P.S.T. Switch.
V1—Clairex CL-3 Photocell.

Courtesy Sylvania Electric Products, Inc.

Photo-relay circuit.

used for the second stage. Transistors Q2 and Q3 function as a trigger circuit. The characteristic of this circuit is such that when the base voltage of Q2 is above a certain value; Q2 is cut off. When the base voltage of Q2 is below this value, Q3 then conducts a large current which closes the relay. Only a very small change in voltage on the base of Q2 is required to switch the relay.

R1 is used for adjustment and, with light falling on the photocell, R1 is set to the point where the relay opens and a slight decrease in the amount of light will close the relay. A certain amount of experimentation is needed to set the relay at the proper point, depending on operating conditions for the particular application.

PHOTOELECTRIC COMPARATOR

The photoelectric comparator is a balanced light-sensitive bridge that indicates any unbalance in light intensity applied to the two photoelectric cells. The comparator can serve in a number of applications, such as determining the difference in color of two objects which have an otherwise similar surface. The color difference produces a difference in reflected light from the two objects, provided that they are equally well illuminated and the cells are held the same distance away. The comparator can also be used to detect people passing through doorways, the passage of electric trains in a model railroad setup, the opening and closing of doors, etc. The photoelectric comparator is far superior to conventional photoelectric circuits for many applications; conventional photoelectric circuits require a constant resetting of the sensitivity control as the daylight background changes.

With no illumination the resistance of the photocells is very high—greater than 1 megohm. Since all of the components in each transistor

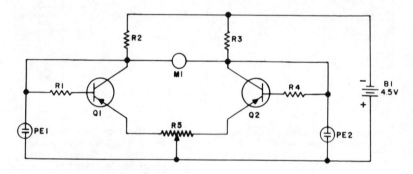

Q1, Q2 — Sylvania 2N1266 transistor
R1, R4 — 120 k, ½ w
R2, R3 — 680 Ω, ½ w
R5 — 5 k potentiometer, ½ w

B1 — 4.5-volt battery
M1 — 1 ma d-c meter, zero-centered
PE1, PE2 — Sylvania CDS-9M
    photo-electric cell

Courtesy Sylvania Electric Products, Inc.

Photoelectric comparator.

circuit are identical, a balanced condition exists when no light is present or when light of the same intensity is applied to each photoelectric cell. When the circuit is in a balanced condition, resistor R5 is adjusted for a zero indication on meter M1.

If the light intensity applied to photoelectric cell PE1 is decreased, its resistance will increase considerably, causing an unbalance of the bridge circuit and increasing the collector voltage of Q1. If the light intensity applied to photoelectric cell PE2 is not changed, the increased voltage at the collector of Q1 will cause current to flow through meter M1.

WIRELESS REMOTE PHOTO FLASH

The wireless, remote, photo-flash unit is used to supplement the regular flash unit on a camera. The remote unit is triggered by the flash of the regular camera. When properly located, the wireless, remote, photo-flash unit will add depth and detail to a picture which cannot be obtained with a single flash bulb. The remote flash unit operates when the flash is received at the sun battery. A direct-coupled wideband amplifier amplifies the sun-battery voltage and fires a conventional battery-capacitor firing circuit. The wide-band amplifier provides a fast response time, assuring that the slave flash will fire while the camera shutter is still open.

When the flash from the camera is received at the sun battery, a voltage is produced which forward biases transistor Q1. Transistor Q1

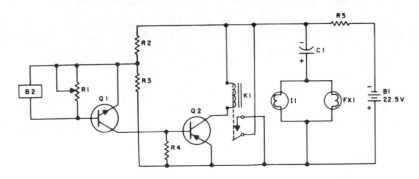

B1 — 22½-volt battery
B2 — Sun battery, International Rectifier
   Corp. Type B2M or equivalent
C1 — 100 mfd electrolytic, 25-volt
FX1 — Flashbulb — any conventional type
   consistent with power supply and socket
I1 — 6-10-volt indicator lamp such as
   #51 or #47

K1 — 500 ohm relay, single-pole,
   single-throw, normally open
   Sigma Type 550 G-11F or equivalent
Q1 — Sylvania 2N229 transistor
Q2 — Sylvania 2N255 transistor
R1 — 10 k, ½ w potentiometer
R2, R3 — 15 k, ½ w
R4 — 470 Ω, ½ w
R5 — 100 Ω, ½ w

Courtesy Sylvania Electric Products, Inc.

Wireless, remote photoflash.

is driven into conduction, providing a bias current at the base of transistor Q2. Potentiometer R1 is the sensitivity control for the circuit. When R1 is adjusted to minimum resistance, the sun-battery output is shorted and no bias current flows through Q1. As the potentiometer is backed off, the loading on the sun battery is reduced, and more of the generated current serves to bias the transistor. Resistors R2, R3, and R4 are bias resistors for Q1 and Q2. When Q1 is driven into conduction, transistor Q2 starts to conduct, and relay K1 is energized.

When K1 is energized, the bias voltage is removed from Q2, cutting off Q2 and de-energizing relay K1. This results in a buzzing action by K1, producing a pulsating DC voltage across capacitor C1 and indicator lamp I1. This pulsating DC voltage produces a current flow through C1 and I1 which flashes the bulb. In normal operation, when relay K1 is open capacitor C1 charges to 22½ volts. When the relay closes, the capacitor discharges, firing the flash bulb.

To adjust the circuit for the light level in a given room, slowly turn the sensitivity control (with the flashbulb removed) until the circuit just starts to make a buzzing sound; indicator lamp I1 will glow. Now turn the control back to a point just beyond that where the indicator light goes out.

VARIABLE PULSE-WIDTH LIGHT-ACTIVATED SWITCH

The single-shot, variable-pulse – width, light-activated switch (LAS) uses a light source to produce a variable pulse-width output. The LAS is a subminiature glass-encapsulated silicon PNPN controlled rectifier possessing characteristics similar to conventional gate-operated, PNPN controlled rectifiers. The LAS is triggered on with incident light energy rather than with an electrical gate current.

When light energy is applied to LAS1, the supply voltage is passed to the load and the pulse-forming network. Capacitor C2 charges rap-

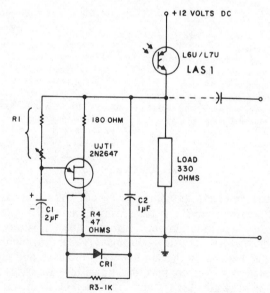

Courtesy General Electric Co.

Light-activated—switch circuit.

idly to the load voltage through resistor R3, and capacitor C1 charges slowly through resistor R1. When capacitor C1 becomes charged to the trigger voltage of unijunction transistor UJT1, the unijunction fires, and C1 is discharged rapidly through resistor R4 and unijunction UJT1. The positive pulse developed across R4 is coupled through diode CR1 and capacitor C2 to the output and to the cathode of LAS1. The result is a pulse output whose width is dependent on the RC time constant of R1 and C1. The variable pulse-width LAS may be used either as a pulser (by differentiating the square-wave output with a capacitor), or as a light-activated time delay (by stretching the output square wave up to several seconds with suitable UJT constants).

VARIABLE ON-TIME SWITCH

The impulse-actuated, variable-on-time switch uses a light-actuated switch (LAS) to apply current to the load and an RC time constant to determine the length of time the current will be main-

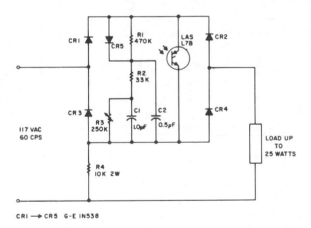

CRI —▶ CR5 G-E IN538

Courtesy General Electric Co.

Variable on-time switch.

tained. During conduction of the LAS, the full sine wave is applied to the load with virtually no harmonic distortion. This circuit is useful for operation of solenoids, contactors, small motors, lamps, etc.

When a light source is applied to the LAS, current is applied to the load. During the positive half-cycle, current flows through the load, diode CR4, LAS, and diode CR1. Capacitors C1 and C2 charge through CR5 during this half-cycle. During the negative half-cycle, current flows through diode CR3, the LAS, diode CR2, and the load. Capacitors C1 and C2 discharge through resistors R2, R3, R1, and the

LAS. As long as this capacitor-discharge current is higher than the holding current, LAS cannot commutate. When the discharge current drops below the holding current, LAS turns off at the next succeeding current zero, assisted by resistor R4 for inductive loads. Decreasing the value of R3 reduces the time the switch remains on. This switch can turn on at any phase angle, but it will turn off only at zero current.

"WORLD'S SMALLEST PHASE CONTROL"

This circuit consists of two light-actuated switches (LAS's), a miniature No. 2128 lamp, and a variable resistor. The circuit is very useful for small heating elements, such as a soldering iron or for lamp dimming except at the low end of the range where flickering occurs as

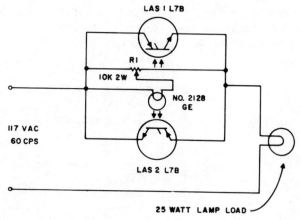

Courtesy General Electric Co.

Circuit of "world's smallest phase control."

the result of changes in lamp resistance. The light-activated switch is a subminiature glass-encapsulated silicon PNPN switch that possesses characteristics similar to conventional gate-operated PNPN controlled rectifiers. The LAS is triggered on with incident light energy, rather than with an electrical-gate current.

Light-activated switches LAS1 and LAS2 are connected back to back so that AC can pass. When current is applied to the circuit, the source voltage is dropped across resistor R1 and the external load. The voltage across the No. 2128 lamp is dependent on the setting of R1. With a low voltage applied to the lamp, the time to reach the LAS firing level is about three cycles. As the applied voltage is increased, this time is reduced, reaching about 1 millisecond when the lamp is directly across the LAS terminals.

During the positive half-cycle, current flows through the load and LAS1 only after LAS1 is triggered on by the light from the No. 2128 lamp. After the positive half-cycle, the bias on LAS1 is removed and it returns to the Off state. The lamp must now reach the firing level of LAS2 before the negative half-cycle is passed by LAS2 to the load. Therefore the setting of R1 determines the firing level of LAS1 and LAS2. Adjustment of R1 determines the on time of the light-activated switches and consequently controls the voltage applied to the external load.

LAS COUNTING CIRCUIT

The LAS counting circuit uses light-activated switches (LAS's) to trigger a capacitor-commutated, controlled-rectifier (SCR), flip-flop circuit with an electromechanical-counter load in one leg. The counter shifts one digit each time the flip-flop goes through one full cycle. With suitable selection of components the circuit may be used to power a variety of DC loads, such as relays, stepping motors, lamps,

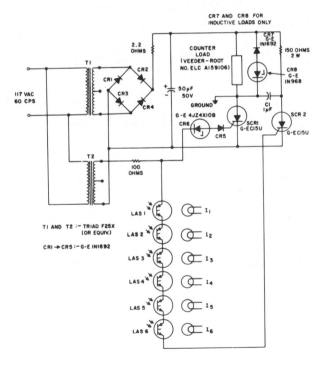

Courtesy General Electric Co.

LAS counting circuit.

117

etc. With slight variations it is also useful in many monitoring, control, and alarm applications.

The 117-volt AC, 60-cycle input is applied through transformer T1 to fullwave rectifier diodes CR1 through CR4. The output of the rectifier is applied to the flip-flop circuit composed of silicon-controlled rectifiers SCR1 and SCR2. With all the light-activated switches on, SCR2 conducts, since it receives a gate signal through the LAS string from transformer T2.

Controlled rectifier SCR1 cannot fire because the conducting-voltage drop across the string of LAS plus the gate voltage of SCR2 is lower than the breakdown voltage of zener diode CR6. When any of the light beams are broken, however, one of the LAS's will cease to conduct, since the AC voltage from T2 makes them self-commutating, and the gate voltage is removed from SCR2. Voltage then rises across CR6 until it conducts and triggers SCR1. SCR1 then activates the counter. The circuit resets when all light beams are restored to the LAS string.

PRODUCTION-LINE FLOW MONITOR

This circuit is used to monitor the smooth flow of small components down a high-speed conveyor chute. It has the capability of "overlooking," or passing up, small self-clearing pile-ups, but it will shut the

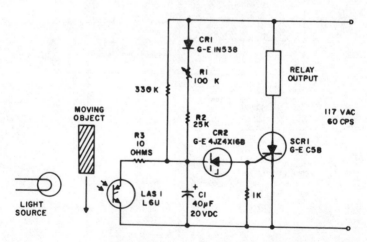

Courtesy General Electric Co.
Production-line, flow-monitor circuit.

line down rapidly in the event of an impending catastrophic "jam." When light-activated switch LAS1 has been interrupted for a sufficient length of time for a gating voltage to develop on controlled recti-

118

fier SCR1, the SCR will be triggered on, and 117 volt AC is applied across the relay.

During the normal flow of moving objects past LAS1, the switch is briefly commutated by the 60-cps AC line voltage. During these off periods, capacitor C1 starts to charge toward the peak AC line voltage through R1, R2, and CR1, but it is shorted to zero once more as light is restored to LAS1. However, should there be a pile-up, the light path to LAS1 is blocked for more than a few milliseconds, and capacitor C1 continues to charge unimpeded by LAS1. At some time determined by the time constant of C1, R1, and R2 the voltage across C1 will exceed the avalanche voltage of zener diode CR2 and fire controlled rectifier SCR1. SCR1 then activates the load. Reset is automatic when light is restored to LAS1. The delay time can be adjusted from a few milliseconds up to several seconds by adjustment of R1.

SLAVE FLASH

In the photographic industry there is a need for a fast photo-sensitive switch capable of triggering the slave flash units used extensively in multiple-light, high-speed photography. This circuit shows how an industry-standard flash-gun circuit can be modified with a light-activated switch (LAS) to serve as a fast-acting slave unit.

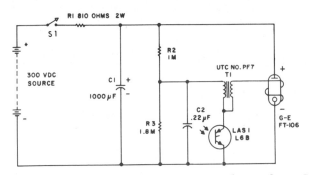

Courtesy General Electric Co.

Circuit for slave-flash unit.

With switch S1 closed, capacitor C1 charges to 300 volts through resistor R1, and capacitor C2 charges to approximately 200 volts through resistors R2 and R3. When the master flash gun fires (triggered by the flash contacts on the camera), its light output triggers LAS1. LAS1 is switched on, and capacitor C2 discharges through LAS1 and the primary winding of transformer T1. The secondary of T1 produces a high-voltage pulse to trigger the flash tube. The flash tube discharges capacitor C1, while the resonant action between C2

119

and T1 reverse-biases LAS1 for positive turn-off. With the intense instantaneous light energy available from present-day electronic flash units, the speed of response of the LAS is in the low microsecond region, leading to perfect synchronization between master and slave units.

PHOTOGRAPHY LIGHT METER

This photography light meter can be used by amateur photography fans; it is a simple device to construct. The circuit uses a photodiode to control the base bias on transistor Q1. As the light intensity increases on the photodiode, current through Q1 decreases. As the current through Q1 decreases, the needle on meter M1 moves from

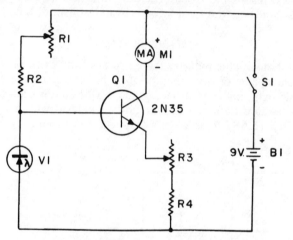

B1 - 9V. Battery, Burgess #2N6 with snap terminals or equivalent.	R2 - 27K, 1/2w. Resistor.
	R3 - 250Ω Potentiometer.
M1 - Meter, 0 to 15 milliamperes D. C.	R4 - 68Ω, 1/2w. Resistor.
Q1 - Sylvania 2N35 Transistor.	S1 - S. P. S. T. Toggle Switch.
R1 - 25K Potentiometer.	V1 - Sylvania 1N77A Photodiode.

Courtesy Sylvania Electric Products, Inc.

Circuit for photography light meter.

right to left in a manner similar to an ohmmeter. A chart of camera settings versus meter readings has to be made through experimentation.

With a low light-intensity level the photodiode is back biased so that its resistance is very high. Therefore the voltage on the diode approaches the battery supply voltage. This positive voltage on the base of transistor Q1 results in heavy conduction. As the light intensity increases, the back resistance of V1 decreases, thus decreasing the positive voltage on the base of Q1, and the current flowing through M1 decreases. At intense light levels the photodiode is a short circuit, and meter M1 reads zero current. At a low intensity R1 and R3 should be adjusted for full-scale deflection of M1. When the photography light meter is mounted on the camera, be sure that there is nothing obstructing the light falling on the photodiode. Also, photodiode V1 must be polarized correctly. The cathode end of the photodiode is indicated by a red dot on the body of the unit.

AC-OPERATED CIRCUITS

Photocell and relay circuits can be operated directly from an AC source either by using an AC relay or a rectifier and a DC relay.

Circuit A shows the use of an AC relay; AC line voltage is applied directly across the variable resistor. Light levels as low as 1.0 foot-candles operate this circuit. The control allows adjustment of the photocell current for relay operation. This circuit is designed

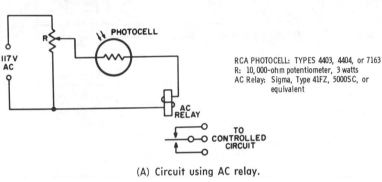

RCA PHOTOCELL: TYPES 4403, 4404, or 7163
R: 10,000-ohm potentiometer, 3 watts
AC Relay: Sigma, Type 41FZ, 5000SC, or
    equivalent

(A) Circuit using AC relay.

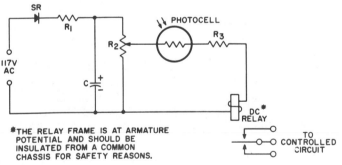

*THE RELAY FRAME IS AT ARMATURE
POTENTIAL AND SHOULD BE
INSULATED FROM A COMMON
CHASSIS FOR SAFETY REASONS.

RCA PHOTOCELL: TYPES 4403, 4404, or 7163
C: 8μf, electrolytic, 250 volts (dc working)
R_1: 5.6 ohms, 1 watt
R_2: 25,000-ohm potentiometer, 5 watts,
    Centralab Type WN, or equivalent
R_3: 10,000 ohms, 1 watt

DC Relay: Sigma, Type 11F-9000G/SIL, or
    equivalent, 9000 ohms, 2.4 ma
    operating current
SR: Silicon Rectifier, RCA-1N1763

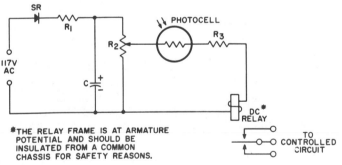

Courtesy Radio Corporation of America.

(B) Circuit using DC relay.
AC-operated relay circuits.

for on-off applications and should not be used where the light level varies gradually, since this causes relay chatter.

Circuit B can be used for gradual changes in light or for an on-off application. A rectifier is used so that a DC relay is applicable to the circuit. This circuit also operates with light levels as low as 1.0 foot-candle.

ANNUNCIATOR SYSTEMS

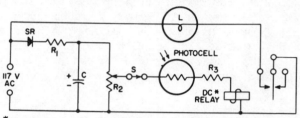

*THE RELAY FRAME IS AT ARMATURE POTENTIAL AND SHOULD BE INSULATED FROM A COMMON CHASSIS FOR SAFETY REASONS.

RCA PHOTOCELL: TYPE 7163
C: 8µf, electrolytic, 250 volts (dc working)
L: 117V AC lamp
R_1: 5.6 ohms, 1 watt
R_2: 25,000-ohm potentiometer, 5 watts, Centralab Type WN, or equivalent
R_3: 10,000 ohms, 1 watt

S: Push-button switch, normally closed, Littel Switch, Type 102, or equivalent
SR: Silicon Rectifier, RCA-1N1763
DC RELAY: Sigma, Type 11F-9000 G/SIL, or equivalent, 9000 ohms, 2.4 ma operating current.

A) Light-activated circuit.

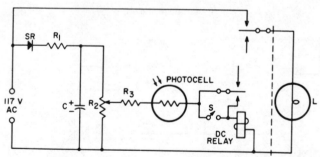

RCA PHOTOCELL: TYPE 7163
C: 8µf, electrolytic 250 volts (dc working)
L: 117V AC Lamp
R_1: 5.6 ohms, 1 watt
R_2: 25,000-ohm potentiometer, 5 watts, Centralab Type WN, or equivalent
R_3: 10,000 ohms, 1 watt

S: Push-button switch, normally open, Littel Switch, Type 101, or equivalent
SR: Silicon Rectifier, RCA-1N1763
DC RELAY: Potter and Brumfield, Type GB11D, or equivalent, 10,000 ohms, 3.53 ma operating current.

Courtesy Radio Corporation of America.

(B) Dark-activated circuit.
Annunciator-system circuits.

Circuit A shows indicator lamp L, which is initially off when the circuit is dark. However, when light falls on the photocell, the relay is energized, and the lamp is then connected across the AC line. This lamp illuminates the photocell so that the lamp remains on until the push buttons is manually reset. When the button is pressed, the circuit opens and the relay drops out. This circuit is activated by the presence of light.

Circuit B shows an annunciator system that responds to darkness. In this circuit, when the photocell is illuminated and the switch is manually set, the photo-current flows through the photocell and through the relay coil as shown. The indicator lamp is off. When the illumination on the photocell is removed, however, the relay opens, connecting the indicator lamp to the AC line. Thus the lamp remains on, even though the photocell is illuminated again, until the circuit is reset by the button which re-energizes the relay.

AUTOMATIC LIGHTING CONTROL

Transistor amplifiers can be used in an automatic lighting control, such as used in automobiles to dim the headlights as an on-

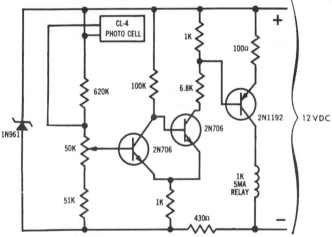

Courtesy Motorola Semiconductor Products, Inc.
Automatic-lighting—control circuit.

coming car approaches. This circuit uses three transistors; two of these are 2N706's and one is a 2N1192 which drives a relay. The photocell is a CL-4. When light hits the photocell, the change in resistance causes a change in the base current of the first 2N706. This is amplified and appears as a change in current which causes the relay to switch the automobile headlights from bright to dim. A zener diode (1N961) is used to regulate supply voltage.

DC-OPERATED PHOTOCELL CIRCUITS

There are various possibilities for simple circuits using direct current sources, such as batteries, for operating photocells and their associated relays.

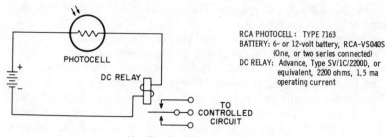

RCA PHOTOCELL : TYPE 7163
BATTERY: 6- or 12-volt battery, RCA-VS040S
(One, or two series connected)
DC RELAY: Advance, Type SV/1C/2200D, or
equivalent, 2200 ohms, 1.5 ma
operating current

(A) Circuit without amplification.

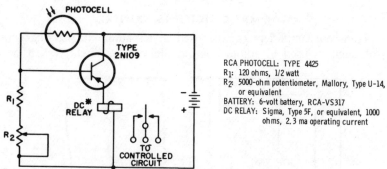

RCA PHOTOCELL: TYPE 4425
R_1: 120 ohms, 1/2 watt
R_2: 5000-ohm potentiometer, Mallory, Type U-14,
or equivalent
BATTERY: 6-volt battery, RCA-VS317
DC RELAY: Sigma, Type 5F, or equivalent, 1000
ohms, 2.3 ma operating current

*THE RELAY FRAME IS AT ARMATURE POTENTIAL AND SHOULD
BE INSULATED FROM A COMMON CHASSIS FOR SAFETY REASONS.

(B) Circuit with transistor amplifier.

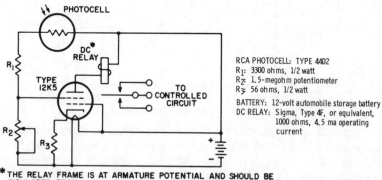

RCA PHOTOCELL: TYPE 4402
R_1: 3300 ohms, 1/2 watt
R_2: 1.5-megohm potentiometer
R_3: 56 ohms, 1/2 watt

BATTERY: 12-volt automobile storage battery
DC RELAY: Sigma, Type 4F, or equivalent,
1000 ohms, 4.5 ma operating
current

*THE RELAY FRAME IS AT ARMATURE POTENTIAL AND SHOULD BE
INSULATED FROM A COMMON CHASSIS FOR SAFETY REASONS.

(C) Circuit with vacuum-tube amplifier.

Courtesy Radio Corporation of America.

DC-operated photocell circuits.

Circuit A uses a type 7163 photocell. This is a very simple circuit that can give direct relay operation without any requirement for circuit amplification. Light falling on the photocell reduces the circuit resistance and increases the circuit current to the point where the relay closes. For 6-volt operation an illumination of about 6 foot-candles is required on the photocell to operate the relay. For 12-volt operation an illumination of about 4 foot-candles is required.

Circuit B shows the use of a type 2N109 transistor as an amplifier. In this particular circuit the relay is activated when light falls on the photocell with illumination levels as low as 0.5 foot-candle. The potentiometer (R2) in the base leg of the transistor circuit allows adjustment of the circuit sensitivity.

Circuit C shows how a photocell can be used with a vacuum-tube amplifier. Here the illumination levels on the photocell can be as low as 0.1 foot-candle. In this circuit the potentiometer (R2) acts as a sensitivity control for the circuit. It is necessary that the 12K5 be shielded so that light from its filament does not fall on the photocell.

SECTION 8

POWER REGULATORS

THREE-PHASE AC CONTROL OF DC POWER

A circuit showing continuous control of the maximum output DC voltage from 0 to 100% is shown. There are essentially three ordinary rectifiers and three silicon-controlled rectifiers. Each of the controlled rectifiers is fired independently by the unijunction-transistor firing circuit associated with it. The firing angle for each phase is controlled by the collector current of Q2, which acts as a charging source for the unijunction emitter capacitor. The collector current of Q2 is controlled by transistor Q1, and, consequently, the change in the firing angle is proportional to the change in the DC control voltage at the base of transistor Q1. This circuit allows complete control of the DC output voltage over the entire range from 0 to the maximum available from the circuit.

ALTERNATOR REGULATOR

Where alternating-current generators are used, as for battery charging or with emergency power supplied, it is necessary to regulate the output voltage of the generator within reasonable tolerances. This circuit is for a 12-volt, 3-phase, automobile-type alternator. The circuit can be adapted as shown for any number of phases.

A certain portion of the DC voltage is taken across resistor R2, and, when this voltage is less than the zener reference voltage, transistor Q is forward-biased and conducts. This causes the controlled rectifier to fire and apply voltage to the field of the alternator. Note that the rectifier and the field are connected in series across diode CR3. When this diode is reverse-biased, the

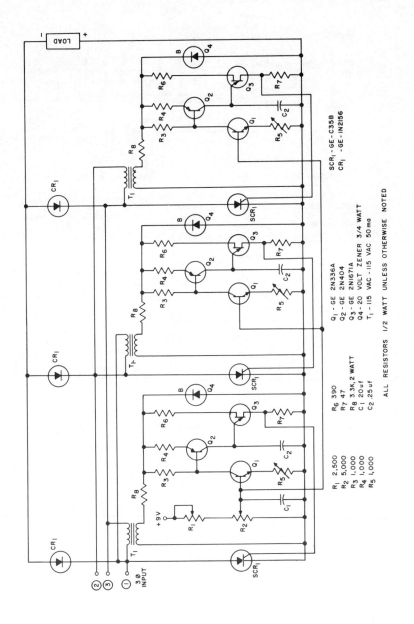

Circuit for three-phase AC control of DC power.

127

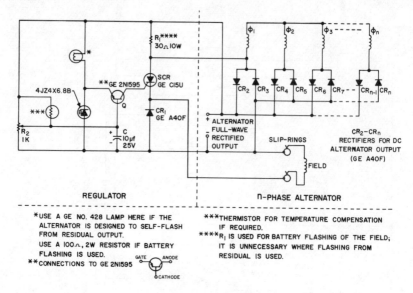

Circuit for alternator regulator.

anode of the rectifier is positive and voltage is applied to the field. When the voltage across the combination of the controlled rectifier and the field reverses polarity, the rectifier turns off and CR1 allows current to continue flowing in the field. When the voltage on the tap of R2 increases beyond the zener voltage, Q is turned off, preventing the rectifier from turning on and consequently cutting back the field current. Resistor R1 is used to allow some current from the battery to flow through the field initially. Capacitor C eliminates hash. With this circuit and a 6-to-1 speed range, the output voltage changes less than 0.2 volts from a 14.0 volt setting at 1,500 rpm with no load.

SHUNT-WOUND DC-MOTOR SPEED REGULATOR

This is a full-wave, speed-regulating circuit for a shunt-wound DC motor. The transistor senses the back emf of the motor and controls the firing of the SCR, which is in series with the armature of the motor. Applications of such a circuit include machine tools, conveyors, printing presses, woodworking machines, and other similar types of apparatus using shunt motors. An avalanche diode (Z1) is used to regulate the supply voltage to the firing circuit.

C2 charges through resistor R3 when the circuit is first turned

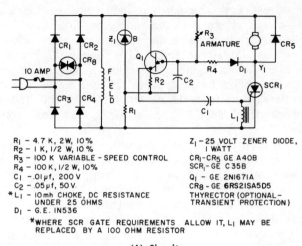

(A) Circuit.

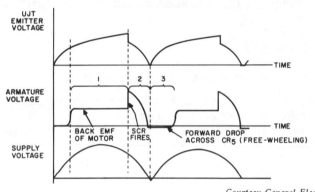

Courtesy General Electric Co.

(B) Waveforms.
DC-motor, speed-regulator circuit.

on, and unijunction transistor Q1 fires when the voltage across
C2 reaches the proper value. Diode D1 is used to prevent charging current from coming through the armature and R4. When
Q1 conducts, a pulse is fed to SCR1 through capacitor C1. The
supply and the avalanche diode provide the return path. When
the SCR1 conducts, a voltage is applied across the armature so
that the motor will rotate.

In part B of the illustration, region 1 of the armature-voltage
waveform shows the back electromotive force of the motor. In
region 2, when the controlled rectifier conducts, the line voltage
is applied to the armature. At the point where the line voltage
decreases through 0, the SCR turns off. There is then a free-

wheeling current flow through the inductance of the armature and CR5—this is region 3 in the waveform. Note that the armature voltage is slightly negative due to the drop across diode CR5. Because of this, D1 is blocked, and capacitor C2 charges at a maximum rate. At the beginning of region 1, the armature-voltage polarity reverses. This forward biases D1 and allows the charging current to be shunted from the capacitor through R4. The amount of current shunted from C2 depends on the back emf of the motor.

When a load is applied to the motor, the motor slows down and draws more current, which effectively widens region 3 since there is now more current to decay through CR5. This allows the charging current to flow into capacitor C2 for a longer period of time. Because the back emf is reduced, the amount of charging current which is shunted through R4 during region 1 is also reduced. Because of both of these effects, C2 is charged faster, and region 2 is widened. This is the voltage pulse which is applied to the armature by the SCR firing. Capacitor C2 discharges through resistor R4 during region 2 when the cathode of diode D1 is connected to the negative supply through the conducting controlled rectifier SCR1.

ALTERNATOR VOLTAGE REGULATOR

This circuit shows two transistors used in an alternator voltage regulator for automobiles. One transistor (Q1) is a 2N2137 and the second transistor (Q2) is a 2N1539. In this circuit, the zener diode conducts and allows base current flow through transistor Q1 when the battery voltage has reached the voltage-regulator setting. When this diode conducts, it turns transistor Q2 off, interrupting the current flow through the alternator field, which, in turn, cuts off the alternator charging current to the battery.

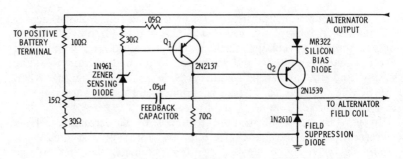

Circuit for alternator voltage regulator.

When the battery discharges below the set voltage, the sensing diode switches off Q1 and allows Q2 to again energize the alternator.

ZENER-REGULATED, MOTOR-SPEED CONTROL

The zener-regulated, motor-speed control utilizes an inherent speed feedback which provides essentially constant speed characteristics adequate for many different types of applications over a wide range of speed. Typical uses for this circuit are: fans, blowers, ventilating equipment, hobby and toy applications, hand tools, home appliances, etc. The circuit can be used wherever a wide range of speed is required from a universal (series) motor operating from a single-phase AC line. The circuit is compact and can often be fitted into the motor housing or end cover.

The speed of the motor is determined by the length of time controlled rectifier SCR1 conducts during each cycle. When the line voltage is negative, the series field of the motor is excited through R3 and CR3. This induces a negative voltage in the armature that is proportional to the speed of the motor and the field strength. The negative armature voltage charges capacitor C1 through CR2 and the gate of SCR1 so that the top terminal of C1 becomes negative with respect to the bottom. When the line voltage swings positive, C1 discharges through R1 at a rate dependent on the time constant of C1 and R1. When V_c swings positive, SCR1 is fired by the gate current that now flows through CR2, and the line voltage is applied to the motor.

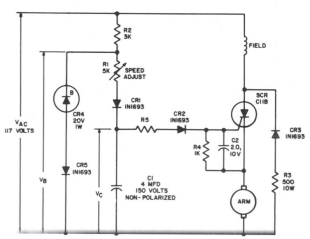

Courtesy General Electric Co.

Motor-speed control circuit with zener regulation.

V_c reaches the triggering level of SCR1 at a phase angle determined partly by the setting of R1. If a heavy load is applied to the motor, it tends to slow down, thus reducing the induced armature voltage and limiting the peak negative value of V_c to a lower level. V_c therefore discharges sooner than under no load conditions, swinging positive and firing SCR1 at a smaller angle. This advance in the firing angle increases the voltage applied to the motor and delivers additional torque to the motor to compensate for the increased load. Zener regulator CR4 provides a constant voltage for the discharge of C1. The desired speed setting is adjusted by R1. C2 and R4 stabilize the circuit by preventing SCR1 from being fired by extraneous signals.

MOTOR-SPEED CONTROL

This motor-speed control utilizes an inherent speed feedback which provides essentially constant speed characteristics adequate for many different types of applications over a wide range of

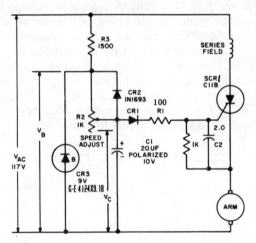

Courtesy General Electric Co.

Motor-speed control.

speed. Typical uses for this circuit are: fans, blowers, ventilating equipment, hobby and toy applications, hand tools, home appliances, and so on. This circuit provides stable operation at very low speeds.

During the negative half-cycle of the supply voltage, capacitor C1, which may be of the polarized electrolytic type, is discharged to zero. During the positive half-cycle, C1 charges from a constant potential (zener voltage of CR3) at an exponential rate dependent on the time constant of C1 and R2. If the motor armature is standing still, no voltage is induced in it by the residual field, and gate currrent to controlled rectifier SCR1 flows as soon as V_c exceeds the forward voltage drop of CR1 and the gate drop of SCR1. This will fire SCR1 early in the cycle, providing ample energy to accelerate the motor. As the motor approaches its preset speed, the residual induced voltage in the armature builds up. This voltage is positive on the top terminal of the armature and bucks the flow of gate current from capacitor C1 until V_c exceeds the armature voltage. This higher voltage requirement on C1 retards the firing angle and allows the motor to cease accelerating.

Once the motor has reached operating speed, the residual induced voltage provides automatic speed-regulating action. For instance, if a heavy load starts to pull down the motor speed, the induced voltage decreases, and SCR1 fires earlier in the cycle. The additional energy thus furnished to the motor supplies the necessary torque to handle the increased load. Conversely, a light load with its tendency to increase speed raises the motor residual induced voltage, retarding the firing angle and reducing voltage on the motor. Adjustment of R2 provides speed control by controlling the charge time of C1. When R2 is adjusted to a low value V_c builds up fast and fires SCR1 early in the cycle. When R2 is set to a large value, V_c builds up slowly so that firing occurs late in the cycle and the motor speed is low. This circuit can be used wherever a wide range of speed is required from a universal (series) motor.

SCR FLUORESCENT-DIMMER 1

The silicon-controlled rectifier (SCR) flourescent dimmer circuit provides remote manual control of fluorescent lamp brightness. One SCR dimmer can control a large number of ballast/lamp combinations. The control circuit is a basic unijunction transistor-SCR trigger circuit adapted to the requirements of fluorescent lamp dimming. The zener diode regulated supply helps provide a smooth control characteristic over the entire dimming range. The control circuit features ON and OFF trim potentiometers. As the lamps used in an installation age (after 100 hours or so of operation) the dimming range may easily be expanded by the use of these trimmers.

Resistors R3 and R1 in the control circuit feed back a portion of the line supply voltage to base 2 of unijunction transistor UJT1. Capacitor C2 will charge to the constant potential provided by zener diode CR5. In this manner the circuit compen-

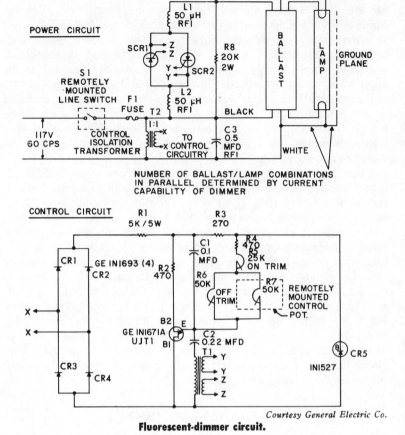

Courtesy General Electric Co.

Fluorescent-dimmer circuit.

sates for line voltage changes over a half-cycle of line frequency by advancing the SCR firing angle when the line voltage drops. It retards the firing angle when the voltage rises. This feature is particularly desirable when the dimmer is operated from power lines subject to voltage regulation.

When remotely mounted line switch S1 is closed, AC voltage is coupled through control isolation transformer T2 to the control circuit. During the positive half-cycle (that is, when the voltage at the junction of CR1 and CR3 is positive), a charging current flows through T1, C2, R6, R7, R5, R4, R3, and R1. When the charge across C2 becomes sufficient to fire unijunction transistor UJT1, C2 discharges through UJT1 and the primary of T2 inducing a voltage in the secondary windings of T2. The phase angle at which UJT1 fires is determined by the time constant

134

of C2 and resistors R1 and R3 through R7. Remotely mounted control potentiometer R7 provides remote control of the firing angle of UJT1. During the negative half-cycle (that is, when the voltage at the junction of CR1 and CR3 is negative), a charging current flows through CR3, T1, R3 through R7, R1, and CR2, again charging C2 until UJT1 is triggered. C2 again discharges through UJT1 and T1 producing a pulse in the secondary windings of T1. These pulses, delayed several degrees depending on the setting of R7, are coupled to the gate circuits of controlled rectifiers SCR1 SCR2. SCR1 and SCR2 are alternately fired on positive and negative half-cycles by the pulses from the control circuit. Since these pulses are delayed, current will be applied to the fluorescent lamp circuit during only part of each cycle. The greater the resistance of R7, the greater is the delay in the pulses and consequently the shorter is the conduction time of SCR1 and SCR2. Therefore, adjustment of R7 controls the brightness of the fluorescent lamps. Inductors L1 and L2 and capacitor C3 form a filter for suppression of radio-frequency interference.

SCR FLUORESCENT-DIMMER 2

This silicon-controlled rectifier (SCR) fluorescent dimmer circuit provides remote manual control of fluorescent lamp brightness. One SCR dimmer can control a large number of ballast lamp combinations. The control circuit is a basic unijunction transistor SCR trigger circuit adapted to the requirements of fluorescent lamp dimming.

During the positive half-cycle (that is, when the voltage at the junction of CR1 and CR3 is positive), a charging current flows

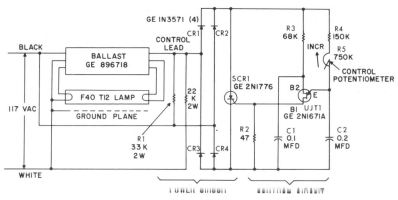

Courtesy General Electric Co.

SCR Fluorescent-dimmer circuit.

135

through CR4, C2, control potentiometer R5, R4, and CR1, charging C2. Simultaneously C1 is charged through R3. When the charge across C2 becomes sufficient to fire unijunction transistor UJT1, C2 discharges through UJT1 and resistor R2 producing a pulse at the gate of controlled rectifier SCR1. SCR1 now conducts for the remainder of the positive half cycle passing current to the fluorescent lamp. At the end of the positive half cycle, the voltage across SCR1 drops to zero and it switches off.

During the negative half-cycle (that is, when the voltage at the junction of CR1 and CR3 is negative), a charging current flows through CR3, C2, R5, R4, and CR2, charging C2. When the charge across C2 becomes sufficient to fire UJT1, C2 discharges through UJT1 and R2 producing a pulse at the gate of SCR1. SCR1 again conducts for the remainder of the negative half-cycle passing current to the fluorescent lamp. At the end of the negative half-cycle the voltage across SCR1 drops to zero, and SCR1 switches off again, thus completing the cycle. By adjusting control potentiometer R5, the charge time of C2 can be varied and the conduction time of SCR1 is controlled. Therefore R5 controls the brightness of the fluorescent lamp. It was found necessary to employ some amount of loading resistance for stability over a wide dimming range, therefore resistor R1 was added to the circuit. The required SCR voltage rating depends on the ballast voltage appearing between the "control" and "black" leads, the loading resistance, and, of course, any voltage transients that may enter the system.

AC PHASE-CONTROLLED SWITCH

This circuit is a fundamental AC control circuit used in lighting and heating (temperature) control, and in voltage regulation. The parallel-inverse, or back-to-back, connected controlled rectifiers provide full-wave phase control from zero to full load current.

During the positive half-cycle (that is, when the voltage at the cathode of CR1 is positive), a charging current flows through CR3, T1, C1, R2, R3, and CR2. When C1 becomes sufficiently charged to trigger unijunction transistor Q1 into conduction, it discharges through T1 and Q1 developing a gate voltage in the primary winding of T1. Zener diode CR5 maintains a constant base 1 - base 2 voltage on Q1. The charge time of C1 and therefore the triggering time of Q1 is determined by the time constant of C1, R2, and R3.

Transistor Q2 shunts some of the charging current supplied

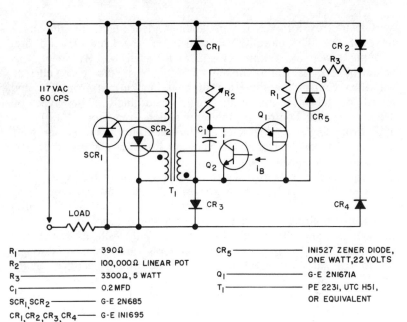

(A) Circuit diagram.

R_1	390 Ω	CR_5	INI527 ZENER DIODE, ONE WATT, 22 VOLTS
R_2	100,000 Ω LINEAR POT		
R_3	3300 Ω, 5 WATT	Q_1	G-E 2NI671A
C_1	0.2 MFD	T_1	PE 2231, UTC H51, OR EQUIVALENT
SCR_1, SCR_2	G-E 2N685		
CR_1, CR_2, CR_3, CR_4	G-E INI695		

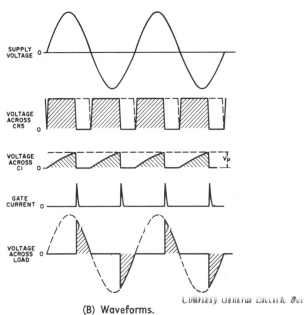

(B) Waveforms.

AC phase-controlled switch.

to C1 by resistor R2 in an amount dependent on the base drive of Q2. The more Q2 is turned on, the later Q1 will fire, and the lower the output of the SCR's will be. By fixing the value of R2 at approximately 2,500 ohms, the base current will then control the diversion of charging current from C1 and retard or advance the firing angle accordingly. This type of shunt transistor control of the unijunction transistor (UJT) and SCR firing angles is characterized by very high gain. Power gain between the base drive of Q2 and the load on the order of 10^8 is readily attainable.

During the negative half-cycle (that is, when the voltage at the cathode of CR1 is negative), a charging current flows through CR1, T1, C1, R2, R3, and CR4. When C1 becomes sufficiently charged to trigger Q1 into conduction, it discharges through T1 and Q1 developing another gate voltage in the primary winding of T1. The gate voltages are coupled through T1 to the gates of SCR1 and SCR2. Controlled rectifiers SCR1 and SCR2 alternately conduct during negative and positive half-cycles respectively. The conduction time of SCR1 and SCR2 can thus be controlled either by adjustment of variable resistor R2 or by adjustment of base current in Q2.

150-WATT VOLTAGE CONTROLLER

This circuit is a fundamental AC control circuit used in lighting and heating (temperature) control, and in voltage regulation. The single controlled rectifier connected in an "SCR in bridge" circuit provides full-wave phase control from zero to full load current.

During the positive half-cycle (that is, when the voltage at the cathode of CR1 is positive), a charging current flows through CR3, capacitor C1, resistors R5, R2, and R3, and diode CR2. Zener diode CR5 provides a constant 20 volts across base 1 and base 2 of unijunction transistor Q1. When the charge on C1 reaches the emitter-base 1 breakdown voltage of Q1, it discharges through R4 and Q1, and a positive pulse is developed at the gate of controlled rectifier SCR1. SCR1 now conducts for the remainder of the positive half-cycle. At the end of the positive half-cycle the voltage across SCR1 drops to zero and it ceases to conduct. During the negative half-cycle (when the voltage at the cathode of CR1 is negative), a charging current flows through CR1, capacitor C1, resistors R5, R2, R3, and diode CR4. Again Q1 fires when C1 becomes sufficiently charged, and a pulse at the gate of SCR1 triggers SCR1 into conduction for the remainder of the negative half-cycle. The charge time of C1, and consequently the firing time of SCR1, is determined by the RC time constant of C1, R5, R2, and R3. Therefore, adjustment of R2 controls the phase angle at which SCR1 fires, re-

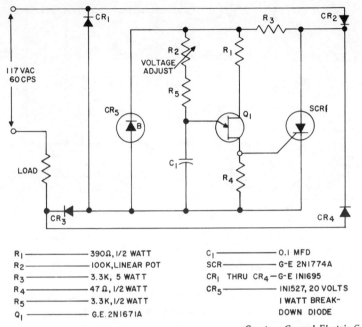

R_1	390Ω, 1/2 WATT	C_1	0.1 MFD	
R_2	100K, LINEAR POT	SCR	G-E 2N1774A	
R_3	3.3K, 5 WATT	CR_1 THRU CR_4	G-E 1N1695	
R_4	47 Ω, 1/2 WATT	CR_5	1N1527, 20 VOLTS	
R_5	3.3K, 1/2 WATT		1 WATT BREAK-	
Q_1	G.E. 2N1671A		DOWN DIODE	

Courtesy General Electric Co.

150-watt, voltage-controller circuit.

sulting in control of the load current. Using the components given in the parts list, this particular circuit is capable of continuously controlling up to 150 watts.

PHASE-SENSITIVE SERVO DRIVE

This circuit is a phase-sensitive servo drive supplying reversible half-wave power to the armature of a small permanent-magnet or shunt motor. The power circuit consists of two half-wave circuits back-to-back fired by a unijunction transistor (UJT). The unijunction transistor fires on either the positive or negative half-cycle of line voltage depending on the direction of unbalance of the reference bridge resulting from the value of the sensing element (R6). The sensing element can be a photoresistor, a thermistor, or an output from a control amplifier.

Potentiometer R2 sets the DC bias on the emitter of unijunction transistor Q2.

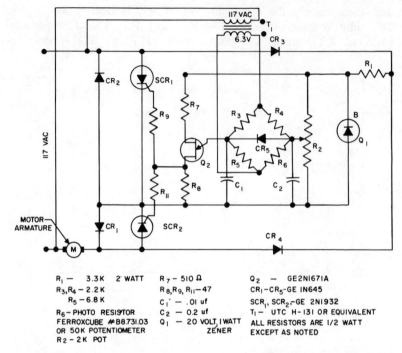

R₁ — 3.3K 2 WATT	R₇ – 510 Ω	Q₂ — GE2N1671A
R₃,R₄ – 2.2 K	R₈,R₉, R₁₁—47	CR₁–CR₅-GE 1N645
R₅ –6.8 K	C₁′ — .01 uf	SCR₁, SCR₂-GE 2N1932
R₆– PHOTO RESISTOR	C₂ – 0.2 uf	T₁ – UTC H-131 OR EQUIVALENT
FERROXCUBE #B8.731.03	Q₁ — 20 VOLT, I WATT	ALL RESISTORS ARE 1/2 WATT
OR 50K POTENTIOMETER	ZENER	EXCEPT AS NOTED
R₂ – 2K POT		

Courtesy General Electric Co.

Circuit of phase-sensitive servo drive.

When R6 is equal to R5, the bridge is balanced, Q2 will not fire, and no output voltage appears across the load. If the value of R6 increases, thus unbalancing the bridge, an AC signal appears at the emitter of unijunction transistor Q2 causing the emitter voltage to be above the firing voltage during one-half cycle of the AC. Q2 fires and, assuming that SCR2 is forward biased, SCR2 fires. Conversely, when R6 is decreased, similar action occurs except that SCR1 fires, reversing the polarity across the load and thus reversing the rotation of the motor.

BATTERY CHARGER

This circuit shows an automatic battery charger using a voltage sensitive switch. The circuit is a Schmitt trigger circuit using two 2N540 transistors. The 2N169A driver is used for increased sensitivity.

When there is a 1-volt drop in the nominal 24-volt battery voltage as sensed by transistor Q1, this transistor conducts through the direct-coupled transistor Q2, turning on the battery charger.

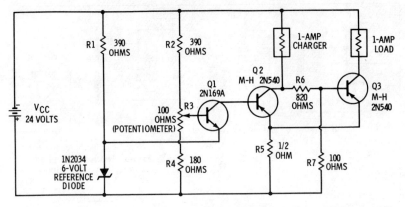

Courtesy Minneapolis-Honeywell Regulator Co.
Battery-charger circuit.

When this happens, transistor Q3 is turned off opening the load circuit. It is possible to adjust resistor R3 for changes in the desired detection voltage level.

PHASE CONTROL OF THE SCR

There are many possibilities for phase control of the silicon-controlled rectifier; often for best matching of the load voltage to the power transmission system a transformer is required between the controlled rectifiers and the load. In circuit A the controlled rectifiers are operating in inverse parallel; the transformer can be used to step the variable output voltage down to a low voltage if desired, for such applications as furnace heating, electroplating, or resistance welding. It is also possible to step the voltage up for such uses as a plate-voltage supply for a transmitter or the plate-voltage supply for an induction-heating tube. In the system shown in circuit B, the transformer is used to drive a bridge rectifier with a filtered output for the DC load.

Circuit C shows the phase control of a four-wire AC system feeding three wye-connected transformers. The input to this circuit is a three-phase AC supply using four wires; three of these are "hot" and one is the neutral.

One pair of controlled rectifiers is connected in series with each of these lines, and the transformer neutral is connnected to the system neutral. Trigger circuits are used from line to neutral for each phase, and a unijunction transistor is used to trigger the pilot controlled rectifiers. Each unijunction circuit is isolated from the power circuit by transformer T3. In this way the three unijunction circuits are electrically interconnected.

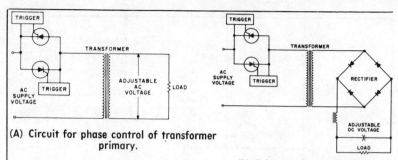

(A) Circuit for phase control of transformer primary.

(B) Primary phase control for adjustable DC power supply.

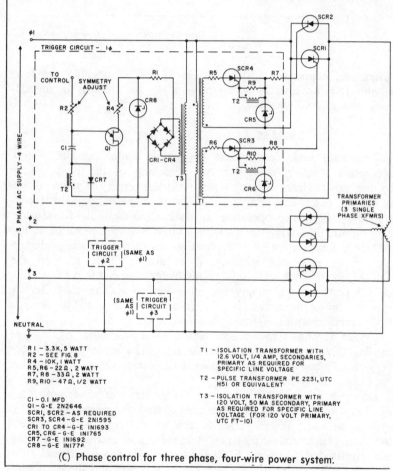

R1 – 3.3K, 5 WATT
R2 – SEE FIG. 8
R4 – 10K, 1 WATT
R5, R6 – 22 Ω, 2 WATT
R7, R8 – 33 Ω, 2 WATT
R9, R10 – 47 Ω, 1/2 WATT

C1 – 0.1 MFD
Q1 – G-E 2N2646
SCR1, SCR2 – AS REQUIRED
SCR3, SCR4 – G-E 2N1595
CR1 TO CR4 – G-E 1N1693
CR5, CR6 – G-E 1N1765
CR7 – G-E 1N1692
CR8 – G-E 1N1776

T1 – ISOLATION TRANSFORMER WITH 12.6 VOLT, 1/4 AMP, SECONDARIES, PRIMARY AS REQUIRED FOR SPECIFIC LINE VOLTAGE

T2 – PULSE TRANSFORMER PE 2231, UTC H51 OR EQUIVALENT

T3 – ISOLATION TRANSFORMER WITH 120 VOLT, 50 MA SECONDARY, PRIMARY AS REQUIRED FOR SPECIFIC LINE VOLTAGE (FOR 120 VOLT PRIMARY, UTC FT-10)

(C) Phase control for three phase, four-wire power system.

Phase control

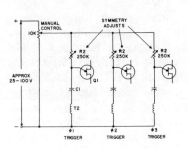

(D) Manual control circuit.

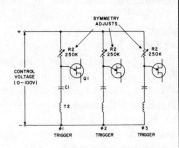

(E) Direct-voltage control circuit.

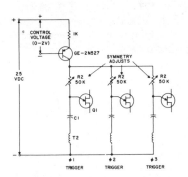

(F) PNP-transistor control circuit.

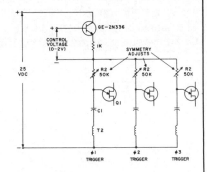

(G) Low-voltage control circuit.

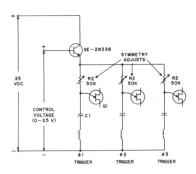

(H) High-voltage control circuit.

Courtesy General Electric Co.

of the SCR.

There are many possible variations for controlling the three unijunctions from the master signal. These are shown in Circuits D through H. The type of circuit used depends on whether a manual or electrical control is required and the magnitude and impedance level of the available control voltage. There are adjustments provided in each unijunction circuit to provide symmetrical firing of the phases. Resistor R4 (Circuit C) is set so that all three of the unijunctions trigger at the same emitter voltage. Resistor R2 is then adjusted for equal tracking of all three phases to a single control signal. Care must be taken in designing the power conductors and the supply to provide for a significant amount of current to be carried in the neutral connection.

Circuit D shows a type of manual control used for each of the three unijunctions. Circuit E shows a direct control voltage from 0 to 100 volts used instead of manual control. Circuit F shows the use of a PNP transistor (2N527) to establish the necessary control. The same thing can be done with an NPN transistor as in Circuit G. High-voltage control is shown in Circuit H.

SECTION 9

AMPLIFIERS

LOW-NOISE FIELD-EFFECT—TRANSISTOR AMPLIFIER

The C620 series of field-effect transistors can be used for very low-noise amplifying applications for such devices as infrared detectors. The field-effect transistor consists of an N-type silicon bar having two ohmic contacts. One of the contacts acts as a cathode and the other acts as the anode. There are two PN junctions constructed in the middle of the bar; these are connected in parallel to serve as the grid. Hence, this solid-state device acts as a vacuum tube in its operation and application.

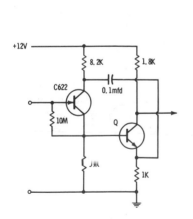

(A) Circuit diagram.

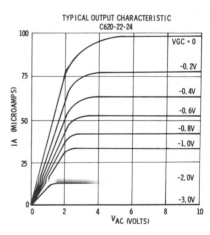

Courtesy Crystalonics, Inc.

(B) Characteristic curves.

Low-noise field-effect transistor amplifier.

145

When a negative voltage (bias) is applied to the grid, there is an increase in the effective resistance from anode to cathode. When the anode voltage is increased, the grid junctions become reverse-biased, and the gain characteristic curve flattens off as shown and resembles that of the pentode vacuum tube.

The diagram shows a low-noise, field-effect, bootstrap amplifier that uses a 12-volt supply. Essentially it is intended for very low-frequency applications. Such circuits, however, may be effectively used up to several hundred kilocycles if desired. A typical gain-bandwidth product for this circuit is 1 mc. The field-effect transistor, as shown, is a C622, while transistor Q can be any low-frequency transistor. The degenerative feedback using the cathode resistor increases the input impedance; this circuit also reduces the grid-to-anode capacitance by feeding the signal back to the anode. The second, or output, transistor provides the necessary low output-impedance drive.

HIGH-VOLTAGE FIELD-EFFECT—TRANSISTOR AMPLIFIER

The C631-C633 series of high-voltage, silicon, field-effect transistors are used for amplifying and switching applications. They have a very high input impedance and are treated in the circuit as vacuum tubes rather than transistors. They are used for such applications as cathode-ray–tube deflection drivers, photo-multiplier drivers, high-voltage switches, or in high-voltage regulated power supplies. The anode-to-cathode voltage and the anode-to-grid voltage vary from 150 volts for the C631 to 350 for the C633; these units are designed to give a voltage gain of at least 10, and they are completely cut off with a grid voltage of 25 volts negative. Note that the circuits resemble very closely those which are used in vacuum-tube circuits. They are compatible, in many ways, with standard vacuum-tube circuits and power supplies.

FIELD-EFFECT TRANSISTOR AMPLIFIER

The amplifier shown in the diagram illustrates the use of a composite, field-effect transistor amplifier which has a number of industrial applications. This circuit uses one of a series of transistor units that are high-transconductance and high-input–impedance, field-effect transistors; each unit is a matched combination of a standard field-effect transistor and an NPN transistor.

In effect this is a transistor circuit that is equivalent to a vacuum-tube amplifier circuit; hence, the electrodes are indicated as grid, anode, and cathode. There are five types in this series; they are the C640 through C644. The gain-bandwidth product for these units varies from between 10 and 20 for the C640 and to between 40 and 60 for the C644 (the gain-bandwidth product is the stage gain multiplied

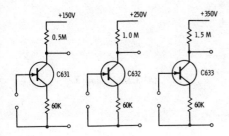

(A) Circuit Diagrams.

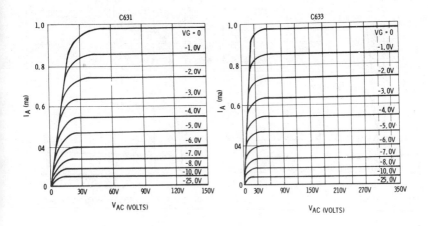

(B) Output Characteristics.

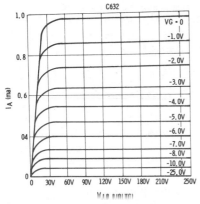

Courtesy Crystalonics, Inc.

High-voltage field-effect – transistor amplifiers.

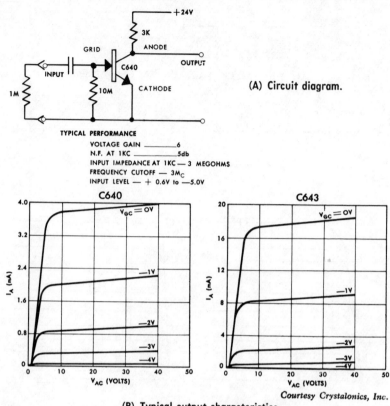

(A) Circuit diagram.

TYPICAL PERFORMANCE

VOLTAGE GAIN _____6
N.F. AT 1KC _____5db
INPUT IMPEDANCE AT 1KC — 3 MEGOHMS
FREQUENCY CUTOFF — 3M$_C$
INPUT LEVEL — + 0.6V to —5.0V

Courtesy Crystalonics, Inc.

(B) Typical output characteristics.
Field-effect transistor amplifier.

by the bandwidth with the result expressed in megacycles). In the standard circuit, as shown, with the 24-volt positive supply, there is a voltage gain of 6. These units have a maximum anode-to-cathode voltage of 35 volts, maximum anode-to-grid voltage of 35 volts, and a maximum grid-to-cathode voltage of −15 volts.

LOW-DRIFT DC AMPLIFIERS

Drift-free DC amplifiers are not a simple design problem; however, by making use of the ST1026 silicon transistor, which has considerable gain at extremely low collector currents, straight DC amplifiers can be constructed that have a very small equivalent input drift with variations in ambient temperature.

Current compensation of the type illustrated in Circuit A is basic to all these straight-DC amplifiers. Base bias current of the first transistor is slightly dependent on temperature, since it is derived through

148

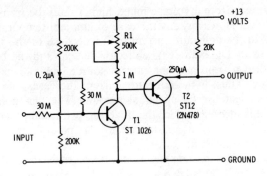

(A) Basic circuit with current compensation.

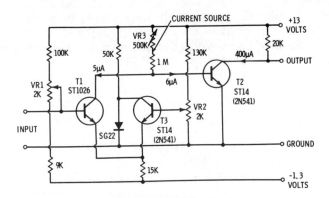

(B) Circuit with compensation for voltage drift.

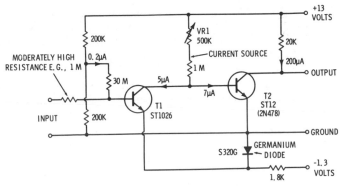

(C) Circuit with compensation for current drift and approximate compensation for voltage drift.

Courtesy Transitron Electronic Corp

Low-drift DC-amplifier circuits

a high resistance from a voltage much higher than the transistor base-emitter voltage. However, any increase of ambient temperature causes an increase in the collector current of T1 because of the temperature coefficient of its DC beta. This collector current and the base current of T2 are drawn from another current source, R1 and its associated fixed resistor. Thus, if the collector current increases, the other base current must decrease by an equal amount. The bias conditions are such that this decrease and the increase with temperature of the DC beta of T2 result in as little change as possible in the collector current of that transistor.

If you know the parameters of the two transistors, such as beta temperature coefficients, dependence of the betas on collector current, etc., it is possible to calculate the value of I_{b2} necessary to achieve these balance conditions for a chosen I_{c1}. Alternatively, with the selected value of I_{c1} fixed by the large resistor in the base lead of T1 (Circuit A), the desired I_{b2} can be determined experimentally, using R1 for adjustment. Voltage-amplifier circuit B has the differential transistor (T3) used to balance the temperature coefficient of T1. Circuit C shows a current amplifier with approximate voltage compensation. This circuit is based on the same principles as the two other types; however, it uses a germanium diode to provide a simpler, but less accurate balancing out of voltage-temperature drift.

INTERCOM

This simple three-transistor intercom consists of one master station and one remote station with a push-to-talk switch at each station. The master station contains a speaker, input-output transformer, amplifier, battery, and push-to-talk switch. The remote station contains a speaker, input-output transformer, and battery. If the positive terminal of each battery is grounded to a water pipe or radiator, only three wires are needed between the master and remote station. When neither push-to-talk switch is depressed, batteries B1 and B2 are disconnected from the circuit, thus eliminating battery drain when the unit is not in operation.

To make a call from the master station, depress push-to-talk switch SW1. This places battery B1 in the circuit to power the amplifier and also connects the secondary winding of transformer T1 to the input of the amplifier. Speaker SP1 now functions as a microphone, converting the voice waves to electrical energy. The signal is coupled through T1 and capacitor C1 to the base of transistor Q1. The signal from the collector of Q1 is developed across collector load resistor R2 and coupled through capacitor C2 to the base of Q2.

The amplified signal from the collector of Q2 is developed across collector load resistor R5 and direct-coupled to the base of Q3. The amplified signal from the collector of Q3 is coupled through trans-

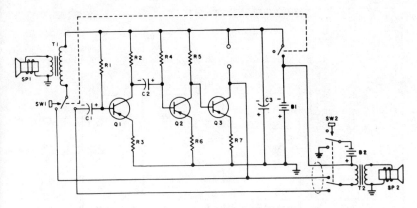

B1, B2 — 9-volt battery
C1, C2, C3 — 25 mfd, 12-volt
Q1, Q2, Q3 — Sylvania 2N1265
R1, R4 — 560 k, ½ w
R2, R5 — 4.7 k, ½ w

R3, R6 — 100 Ω, ½ w
R7 — 1000 Ω, ½ w
SW1, SW2 — DPDT pushbutton switch
SP1, SP2 — 3.2 Ω. 4-inch PM speaker
T1, T2 — 2000 Ω to 3.2 Ω, output transformer,
   Lafayette Radio TR 93

Courtesy Sylvania Electric Products, Inc.

Intercom circuit.

former T2 to remote speaker SP2 and converted to an audible voice sound.

To make a call from the remote station, depress push-to-talk switch SW2. This places battery B2 in the circuit to power the amplifier and also connects the secondary winding of transformer T2 to the input of the amplifier. The signal is coupled through C1 and Q1 and amplified by Q1, Q2, and Q3 in the same manner as when the master station is used. The amplified signal from the collector of Q3 is coupled through T1 to master speaker SP1 and converted to an audible sound.

LOW-LEVEL DC AMPLIFIER

This circuit uses ten RCA 2N1481 medium-power transistors in a DC amplifier. Q9 and Q10 form an inverter, or square-wave generator, operating at 4kc from a 12-volt source. There are three secondary windings, each with its square-wave output.

Winding 1-2 goes to the chopper stage where the DC input (range from ±5 to ±50 millivolts) is converted into AC by Q1 and Q2. A two-stage AC amplifier (Q3 and Q4) follows; this feeds transformer T1.

Windings 3-4, 5-6 from the inverter are tied to the demodulator; Q5 and Q6 form one pair, and Q7 and Q8 form the second pair. The balanced circuit removes or demodulates the square wave, producing a DC output voltage in the ±1 to ±10 volt range. Voltage gain for the circuit is 200.

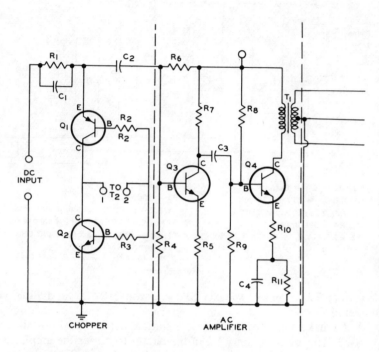

C1: 5 μf

C2: 10 μf

C3: 10 μf

C4: 10 μf

Q1-Q10, inclusive: RCA-2N1481 medium-power
silicon transistors

R1: 510 ohms

R2, R3, R9: 1000 ohms

R4, R7: 2000 ohms

R5: 91 ohms

R6: 20000 ohms

R8: 5000 ohms

R10: 120 ohms

R11: 50 ohms

R12, R13, R14, R15: 500 ohms

R16: 510 ohms

Circuit for low-level

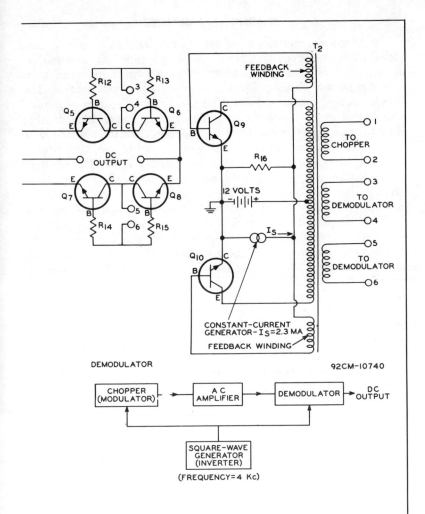

92CM-10740

T_1: Demodulator transformer, primary, 400 turns No. 38 wire; secondary, 1200 turns center-tapped (bifilar wound); core, Allen Bradley Ferrite Pot Core No. C1300-215A (Type RO-3 material) or equivalent.

T_2: Inverter transformer, primary, 70 turns No. 26 wire; center-tapped (bifilar wound); chopper winding, 15 turns No. 30 wire; demodulator windings, each 30 turns No. 30 wire; feedback winding, 30 turns No. 30 wire, center-tapped (bifilar wound); core, Allen Bradley Ferrite Toroid No. T-1312-103A, (Type RO-3 material) or equivalent.

Courtesy Radio Corporation of America.

DC amplifier.

TELEPHONE AMPLIFIER

The telephone amplifier is an audio amplifier that is used to convert the low-amplitude telephone signals to a sufficient amplitude to drive a speaker. The telephone amplifier is convenient when more than one person wishes to listen in on a telephone conversation. This circuit enables you to perform these functions without any electrical connections to the telephone lines. The speaker can be placed either close to or at some distance from the telephone, pickup, and amplifier.

The telephone-pickup coil, placed on the telephone, converts the magnetic telephone voice waves to an electrical signal. The electrical voice signal is coupled through capacitor C1 to the base of transistor Q1. Resistors R1 and R2 are base-bias resistors. Capacitor C2 is a decoupling capacitor. The amplified voice signal from the collector of Q1 is coupled through transformer T1, gain-adjustment potentiometer R7, and capacitor C4 to the base of Q2. Interstage transformer T1 provides impedance matching between Q1 and Q2. The setting of R7 determines the level of the signal applied to Q2, and consequently, the output amplitude of the telephone amplifier. Resistor R3 is a base-bias resistor for Q2.

The amplified voice signal from the collector of Q2 is coupled through phase-splitting tranformer T2 to the bases of push-pull–amplifier transistors Q3 and Q4. Resistors R4 and R5 are base-bias resistors for Q3 and Q4. Capacitor C5 prevents oscillation. Resistor R6 is an emitter-bias resistor. The amplified, 180° out-of-phase voice signals from the collectors of Q3 and Q4 are coupled through transformer T3 to speaker LS1.

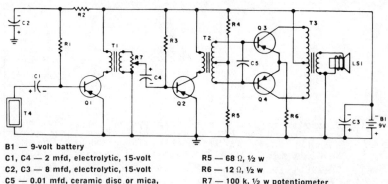

B1 — 9-volt battery
C1, C4 — 2 mfd, electrolytic, 15-volt
C2, C3 — 8 mfd, electrolytic, 15-volt
C5 — 0.01 mfd, ceramic disc or mica, 100-volt
LS1 — 3-6 ohm loudspeaker
Q1, Q2, Q3, Q4 — Sylvania 2N1265 transistor
R1 — 470 k, ½ w   R3 — 270 k, ½ w
R2 — 150 k, ½ w   R4 — 4.7 k, ½ w

R5 — 68 Ω, ½ w
R6 — 12 Ω, ½ w
R7 — 100 k, ½ w potentiometer
T1 — Argonne AR-104, Stancor TA-27, or equiv.
T2 — Argonne AR-109, Stancor TA-35, or equiv.
T3 — Argonne AR-119, Stancor TA-21, or equiv.
T4 — Telephone pickup coil, Lafayette MS-16, Shield M-133, or equiv.

Courtesy Sylvania Electric Products, Inc.

Telephone-amplifier circuit.

The schematic shows one side of the secondary of T3 grounded. This connection is not necessary, but it reduces the possibility of unwanted oscillations in the circuit. Capacitor C3, connected across battery B1, also reduces the possibility of unwanted oscillations. If headphones are to be used, they should be connected between the collector of Q2 and B −.

LIGHT AMPLIFIER

This is not a true light amplifier, because it does not amplify light at its electromagnetic frequency. Rather, the circuit converts light energy into electrical energy, amplifies the electrical energy, and converts the amplified electrical energy back into light energy in a small pilot lamp. The circuit is limited to indicator applications, since only two transistors are used. If high-power stages are used, an entire room can be illuminated with the output of the circuit. The light amplifier can be used as a remote indicator to tell when lights are turned

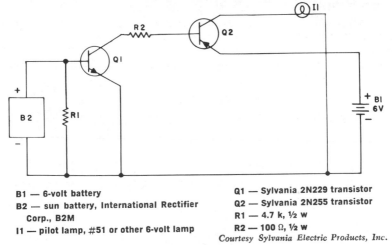

B1 — 6-volt battery
B2 — sun battery, International Rectifier
    Corp., B2M
I1 — pilot lamp, #51 or other 6-volt lamp

Q1 — Sylvania 2N229 transistor
Q2 — Sylvania 2N255 transistor
R1 — 4.7 k, ½ w
R2 — 100 Ω, ½ w

Courtesy Sylvania Electric Products, Inc.

Light-amplifier circuit.

on in another room by placing the light sensing sun battery in one room and the indicator light in another room. The observer can tell by the brightness of the indicator lamp approximately how many lights, if any, are on in the other room. The circuit can also be used as a signaling device by energizing it with a flashlight.

The light amplifier utilizes two grounded-emitter amplifier stages to amplify the voltage sufficiently to drive an indicator lamp. When a light source is applied to sun battery B2, a bias voltage is supplied for amplifier Q1. Resistor R1 develops the bias voltage from B2. The

155

small input current to Q1 is amplified and applied through resistor R2 to the base of amplifier Q2. Resistor R2 is a current-limiting resistor that protects Q1 and I1 when extremely high light intensities strike the sun battery. Q2 must be mounted on a metal panel so that at least 2 inches of metal extends on each side to provide heat-sink action.

The current from the collector of Q1 is amplified by Q2 and applied through indicator lamp I1 back to the negative terminals of the batteries. The intensity of the light applied to the sun battery determines the current through transistor Q1 and, consequently, the current through indicator lamp I1. Thus, the light amplifier not only indicates the presence of light, but it also gives a relative indication of the intensity of light striking the sun battery.

COMPENSATED TRANSISTOR PREAMPLIFIER

The compensated transistor preamplifier is designed for stable performance over a wide temperature range, using a minimum of components. It is primarily intended for a current input and a voltage output. Stabistor DC coupling is used between the amplifier stages to eliminate the need for large bypass capacitors or excessive bleeder current and to prevent any appreciable loss of gain. Sta-

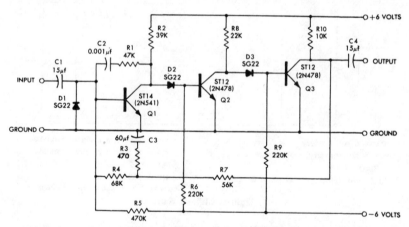

Courtesy Transitron Electronic Corp.
Compensated transistor preamplifier.

bistor coupling also fixes the collector-to-emitter voltages in the first two transistors at a low value (about 1 volt), thereby alleviating the collector current problem and improving reliability.

The input signal is coupled through capacitor C1 to the base of grounded-emitter amplifier Q1. Stabistor diode D1 prevents damage of the base-to-emitter junction by any excessive negative signal.

A portion of the amplified signal from the collector of Q1 is coupled through resistor R1 and capacitor C2 to the base of Q1 as a degenerative feedback signal to prevent high frequency oscillations. The amplified signal from the collector of Q1 is coupled through stabistor diode D2 to the base of grounded-emitter amplifier Q2. The amplified signal from the collector of Q2 is coupled through stabistor diode D3 to the base of grounded-emitter amplifier Q3. The amplified signal from the collector of Q3 is coupled through capacitor C4 to the output. A feedback signal from the output of Q3 to the input of Q1 increases the bandwidth of the preamplifier. Resistors R2, R8, and R10 are collector load resistors. Resistors R5, R6, and R9 are base-bias resistors.

The frequency response of the preamplifier at the 3-db point is 4 cycles to 100 kilocycles, and the maximum undistorted output voltage is 1.0 volt rms. The gain of the preamplifier is 1 volt per 0.125 microvolt, or 44 db with a 50K ohm source and load.

NEGATIVE-IMPEDANCE CONVERTER

It is often difficult to realize a high circuit Q when working with tuned circuits in the lower (audio) frequency range. The difficulty is usually caused by a combination of the low operating frequency and the high series losses associated with inductors. The

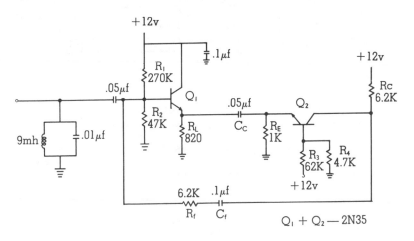

Courtesy Sylvania Electric Products, Inc.
Circuit of negative-impedance converter.

negative-impedance converter reduces circuit losses, thereby increasing the overall Q of the circuit, by adding some negative resistance to the circuit. It is possible to increase the negative resistance up to, but not more than the parallel resistance of the tank circuit. If the negative resistance exceeds the parallel resistance of the tank circuit, oscillations occur.

The signal from the tank circuit is applied through the coupling capacitor to the base of emitter follower Q1. The amplified signal from the emitter of Q1 is coupled through capacitor C_c to the emitter of grounded-base amplifier Q2. The amplified signal from the collector of Q2, in phase with the applied signal, is applied to the base of Q1 as a positive feedback signal. The feedback signal is of sufficient amplitude to improve the Q of the tank circuit without sustaining oscillations. The negative impedance converter is designed to demonstrate Q multiplication. The tank circuit Q in this circuit is multiplied by a factor of 14, giving an overall circuit Q of 20. A much higher multiplication may be obtained, the limit being the condition where the negative resistance equals the parallel coil resistance and oscillations result.

AGC AMPLIFIER USING FIELD-EFFECT TRANSISTOR

This circuit uses a conventional transistor amplifier stage with a field-effect transistor connected in the emitter circuit. Field-effect transistors are characterized by their output characteristic similar to

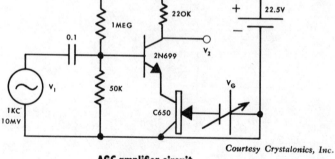

Courtesy Crystalonics, Inc.

AGC-amplifier circuit.

that of the sharp-cutoff vacuum pentode. By varying the grid bias in a field-effect transistor, the transistor will act as a voltage-variable resistance. Variation in grid bias produces a change in resistance from anode to cathode. By using a field-effect transistor as a variable-emitter resistor in an NPN transistor amplifier stage, the stage gain may be controlled.

The 1-kc input signal is coupled through the coupling capacitor to the base of the transistor. Since the base and collector biases are fixed, the gain of the amplifier stage is controlled .by the resistance

158

of the field-effect transistor connected in the emitter circuit of the transistor. The amplified output signal is taken from the collector of the transistor.

DIFFERENTIAL AMPLIFIER

This differential-amplifier circuit is designed as a voltage-controlled, phase-control circuit. The input voltage serves to control the portion of current flowing in each collector. When the applied input voltage reaches a value high enough to cause all of the current to flow in

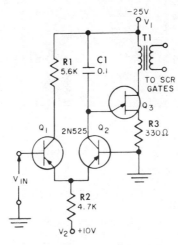

Courtesy General Electric Co.

Differential-amplifier circuit.

the collector of transistor Q1, the input resistance of the circuit increases. The reference voltage for this circuit is zero since the base of transistor Q2 is connected to ground. The use of a PNP transistor gives a more linear control than can be obtained from a NPN transistor.

The charge time for capacitor Cl is determined by the conduction level of transistor Q2. If Q2 is conducting heavily, capacitor Cl charges up rapidly, reaching the emitter-base 1 breakdown voltage of unijunction transistor Q3 at a very small phase angle. When Cl is charged to the triggering voltage, it discharges through Tl, producing a pulse at the secondary of T1. If the voltage is increased at the input, transistor Q1 conducts more heavily, causing the common emitter voltage to become more negative, and the conduction in Q2 is decreased. It is this differential-amplifier action which provides control over the firing angle of Q3. As the con-

159

duction level of Q2 decreases, the charge time of Cl increases and Q3 fires at a larger phase angle.

PULSE AMPLIFIERS

Pulse amplifiers are quite often used as drivers for circuits that fire controlled rectifiers. Two triggering circuits for this purpose are shown here. Direct-coupled circuit A uses a 2N2855 driving a 2N1132. Ex-

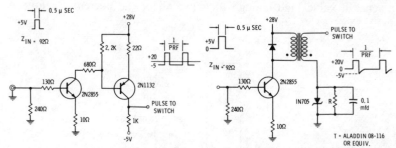

(A) Direct-coupled circuit.

(B) Transformer-coupled circuit.

Courtesy Solid State Products, Inc.

Pulse-amplifier circuits.

ternal bias is used to provide the necessary −5-volt input for the post-trigger period. This circuit and the following one are used to drive controlled rectifiers.

Circuit B uses a pulse transformer and a zener diode network, which, together with the capacitor, provides the necessary bias so an external source is not required. Both of these circuits are triggered by positive-going pulses and both of them have an output to the following power-control circuit.

SECTION 10

POWER SUPPLIES

THREE PHASE, CONTROLLED-RECTIFIER CIRCUIT
FOR DC POWER SUPPLY

The silicon-controlled rectifier offers a convenient means of control for DC power supplies operated from three-phase AC power. Applications of these techniques are useful in such things as temperature controls for electric ovens and furnaces, large incandescent lamp loads, and various other types of DC power-supply requirements. The figure shows a three-phase, 117-volt, AC supply. Diodes CR1 provide a positive line voltage for the control circuit at any time the anode voltage of a controlled rectifier becomes positive in relation to the positive AC bus. By use of a zener regulator (CR2) this voltage is clipped at 20 volts and is used to provide a supply for a unijunction-transistor, relaxation-oscillator firing circuit. Resistor R2 controls the firing angle of Q1 by regulating the charging rate of capacitor C1. When unijunction transistor Q1 discharges capacitor C1, a voltage pulse is developed across resistor R9. This is coupled to the gate lead of each of the three controlled rectifiers through resistors R10, R11, and R12. The controlled rectifier with the most positive anode voltage when the gate pulse appears begins conduction. Transistors Q2 and Q3 are used to prevent Q1 from causing a firing angle greater than 120°. Q3 is a unijunction oscillator that starts its timing cycle at the same moment as Q1. Resistor R1 is adjusted so that Q3 fires at an angle that is less than 120°. When Q3 fires, it causes Q2 to conduct and discharge C1. R2 is the voltage control.

It is important that Q3 keep the firing angle at less than 120°. Base 2 of this unijunction transistor is connected by R5 to resistor R8. This helps to maintain the timing cycle of Q3 less than the required 120° independent of line-voltage variations.

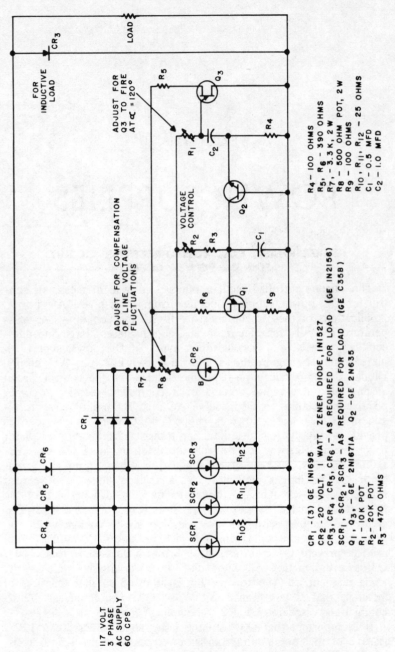

Courtesy of General Electric Co.

DC power-supply circuit.

Base 2 of unijunction transistor Q1 is also connected to R8, also providing compensation for line-voltage variations. For example, with a value of R8 equal to 350 ohms and a load of 10 ohms, a DC load voltage of 92 volts was obtained with a 100-volt AC supply, and a DC load voltage of 93 volts was obtained with a 130-volt AC supply. With this circuit using a three-phase, 117-volt, AC-supply, the output voltage can be varied from 40 volts to 150 volts DC.

PULSE-TRIGGERED IGNITION CIRCUIT

This circuit shows a pulse-triggered ignition circuit that uses a magnetic pickup. There are a number of equally spaced metallic projections which are attached to the distributor shaft in the eng-

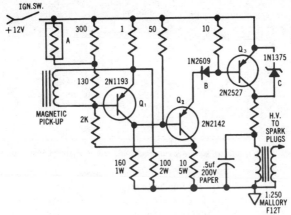

Courtesy of Motorola Semiconductor Products, Inc.

Pulse-triggered ignition circuit.

ine. As these rotate past the magnetic pickup, they produce positive and negative pulses in the pickup. The negative pulses from the magnetic pickup trigger transistor Q1 into conduction and turn off Q2. Transistors Q1 and Q2 make up a bistable multivibrator. Positive pulses coming from the magnetic pickup turn off transistor Q1 and turn on transistor Q2.

Transistor Q3 is used for switching; it turns on and off in synchronism with transistor Q2. Thus transistor Q3 passes or interrupts current flow through the ignition coil primary. Whenever the primary coil current is interrupted, a high-voltage pulse is produced at the secondary of the transformer. This pulse is used to fire the spark plugs. In this circuit transistor Q1 provides a high gain, and transistors Q2 and Q3 are power types. It is necessary that transistor

Q3 have a high enough voltage breakdown to handle the high-voltage pulses which occur in the circuit.

Thermistor A provides a stabilized bias for transistor Q1 and allows reliable operation at low temperatures. Zener diode C is used to protect transistor Q3 against damage from excessive high-voltage spikes which might occur across the ignition coil.

CONSTANT-VOLTAGE POWER SUPPLY

The constant-voltage power supply is designed to limit the variation in DC output voltage to $\pm\frac{1}{2}$ volt with a 20% variation in the input voltage. It uses two controlled rectifiers and a magnetic control unit for the regulation of its output voltage.

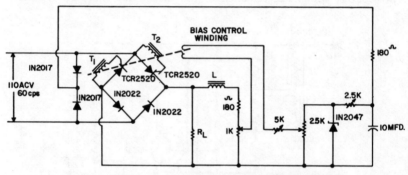

T_1, T_2—Magnetics Inc. Type 4181-001 – FULL WAVE MAGNETIC CONTROL

Courtesy of Transitron Electronic Corp.

Circuit for constant-voltage power supply.

The 110-volt AC input is applied across the full-wave rectifier consisting of two diodes, two controlled rectifiers, and two bias control windings which are part of the magnetic control unit. When a variation in input voltage occurs, it also appears across the load and, consequently, across the 1K ohm potentiometer. This voltage is compared with a reference voltage which appears across the 2.5K ohm potentiometer. When an unbalance exists, current flows through the bias control winding of the magnetic control unit in such a direction as to offset this change. For example, if the input voltage increases, the bias-control–winding current is adjusted so that the firing point of the controlled rectifiers is retarded and a constant-voltage output is obtained. When the line voltage is constant, it is rectified by the full-wave rectifier and filtered by the LR network, with the output voltage dependent on the current through the bias-control winding. By varying the 25K ohm potentiometer the bias current can be changed, thus changing the triggering level of the controlled rectifiers and the output voltage.

10-AMPERE, 400-VOLT RECTIFIER TESTER

The 10-ampere, 400-volt rectifier tester provides meter indication of reverse-supply voltage, reverse leakage current, average forward voltage drop, and average forward current.

For testing reverse leakage current and reverse supply voltage, switch S2 must be closed, applying 110 volts AC to *Powerstat* transformer T1 which is adjusted for the desired reverse sup-

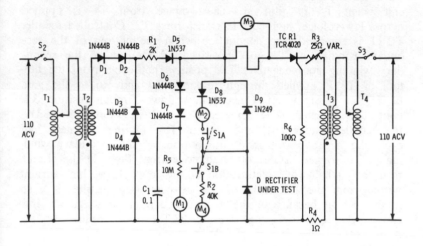

T$_1$, T$_4$ – Powerstats
T$_2$ – 110V/500V
T$_3$ – 110V/30V
M$_1$ – 50 Microamp. movement, 500 Volts peak Full Scale
M$_2$ – 10 Milliamps. Full Scale (Reads full cycle average leakage current)
M$_3$ – 10 Amperes Full Scale (Reads average forward current)
M$_4$ – 50 Microamp. movement, 3 Volts Full Scale (Reads full cycle average forward drop)

S$_{1p}$ – 2 pole momentary contact switch $\left\{ \begin{array}{l} S_{1A} - \text{Normally closed} \\ S_{1B} - \text{Normally open} \end{array} \right.$

Courtesy of Transitron Electronic Corp.

Rectifier-tester circuit.

ply voltage as indicated on meter M1. The voltage from T1 is applied across high voltage, low-current transformer T2. The high-voltage output from T2 is rectified by half-wave rectifier diodes D1 and D2. The rectified voltage produces a DC current through meter M1, resistor R5, diodes D5, D6, and D7, and resistor R1. Meter M1 is calibrated to read reverse-supply voltage with a full-scale reading of 500 volts DC. Capacitor C1 is an

165

AC bypass for the voltmeter circuit. Diodes D6 and D7 protect meter M1 from any negative transient voltages. With the rectifier under test in the circuit, a small, reverse leakage current flows through the test rectifier, switch S1A, reverse leakage-current meter M2, diodes D8 and D5, and resistor R1. Meter M2 indicates the reverse leakage current with a full-scale reading of 10 amp. After completion of this test, switch S2 should be opened.

For testing forward-current and forward-voltage drop, switch S3 must be closed, applying 110 volts AC to T4 which is adjusted for the desired forward current, as indicated on average-forward–current meter M3. The rectifier under test must be in the circuit when T4 is adjusted. The voltage from T4 is applied across low-voltage, high-current transformer T3. Controlled rectifier TCR1 is triggered into conduction when the bottom of the secondary winding of T3 goes positive and the top of the secondary winding goes negative. The positive half-cycle from the bottom of T3 is applied through resistors R4 and R6 to the gate of TCR1, gating it on. Current now flows through resistor R3, controlled rectifier TCR1, meter M3 and its shunt, diode D9, the rectifier under test, and resistor R4. During the next half cycle the negative voltage at the bottom of the secondary winding of T3 triggers TCR1 off, and no current flows in the circuit, resulting in half-wave rectification of the low-voltage, high-current output from the secondary of T3. A controlled rectifier is used in this circuit because of the low voltage required to gate it into conduction. The triggering level of TCR1 is determined by the setting of variable resistor R3. When switch S1 is depressed, meter M4 and multiplier resistor R2 are placed in parallel with the rectifier under test. M4 then indicates the forward voltage drop across the rectifier under test.

6-VOLT POWER SUPPLY

This power supply has a 6-volt filtered and regulated DC output and can supply current up to 1 ampere. Voltage regulation is obtained by using a 6-volt battery to provide base bias on series regulator Q3. When switch S1 is closed, the 115-volt AC source is applied to transformer T1 and stepped down to 6.3 volts AC across each half of the secondary winding. Transistors Q1 and Q2 serve as an efficient full-wave rectifier. The resulting pulsating DC voltage is filtered by capacitor C1.

Transistor Q3 is connected as an emitter-follower series regulator and provides an output which is within a few tenths of a volt of the reference voltage of 6-volt battery B1. Q3 also provides further filtering, thus making the voltage to the load essentially free of ripple. Switch S1B, which is part of the power switch, disconnects B1 from the circuit when the supply is not used. Without R3 in the circuit, some current is drawn from the battery—approximately the load current divided by the collector-to-base current gain of Q3. For example, if the load current were 0.5 ampere and the gain were 20, the battery would supply about 25 milliamperes.

With R3 out of the circuit the output is free of ripple. With R3 in the circuit the battery current may be brought to zero or

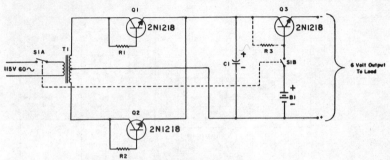

B1—6V. Battery (such as lantern type).
C1—Electrolytic Capacitor, 12V. or greater
   1000 Mfd. for loads to 0.5 amp.
   2000 Mfd. for loads to 1.0 amp.
Q1, Q2, Q3—Sylvania 2N1218 Transistor.
R1, R2—22Ω, ½w. Resistor.
R3—Resistor (see text).
S1—D.P.S.T. Power Switch.
T1—12.6V. C.T. Secondary Transformer (such as Triad F26X).

Courtesy of Sylvania Electric Products, Inc.

Circuit of 6-volt power supply.

even reversed to charge the battery, thus making the life of the battery in the circuit the same as its shelf life. This may, however, introduce a slight amount of ripple into the output, depending on the internal impedance of the battery and the value of R3 used. If the internal impedance of the battery were zero, then the presence of R3 would have no effect.

The proper value of R3 may be determined by measuring the current in B1 with the desired load on the power supply and inserting values of R3 to make the battery current zero or slightly reversed. Or R3 may be a 47-ohm resistor in series with a 250-ohm potentiometer. The ripple introduced depends on the amount of battery current to be balanced out (which is also dependent on load current) and the internal resistance of the battery; it probably will not exceed a few tenths of a millivolt for a ½ ampere load. In building this circuit, mount the transistors on a heat sink.

12-VOLT POWER SUPPLY

This 12-volt power supply provides a filtered and regulated DC output capable of currents up to 1 ampere. By replacing T1 with a transformer having a 6.3-volt secondary (2.5 amp or more rating) and B1 with a 6-volt battery, a 6-volt, 1-ampere bridge-rectifier supply is obtained. All of the transistors should be mounted on heat sinks due to the high currents through them. When switch S1 is closed, the 115-volt AC source is applied to transformer T1 and stepped down to 12.6 volts AC across the sec-

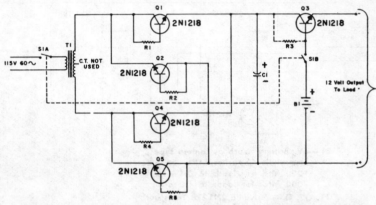

B1—12V. Battery (such as 2-6V. lantern or 2-6V. "A" type).
C1—Electrolytic Capacitor,
   1000 Mfd., 25V. for loads to 0.5 amp.
   2000 Mfd., 25V. for loads to 1.0 amp.

Q1 to Q5 Incl.—Sylvania 2N1218 Transistor.
R1, R2, R4, R5—22Ω, ½w. Resistor.
R3—Resistor (see text).
S1—D.P.S.T. Power Switch.
T1—12.6V. Secondary Transformer (such as Triad F-26X).

Courtesy of Sylvania Electric Products, Inc.

Circuit of 12-volt power supply.

ondary winding. Transistors Q1, Q2, Q4, and Q5 are connected as efficient rectifiers in a bridge-type circuit. The resulting pulsating DC voltage is filtered by capacitor C1.

Transistor Q3 is connected as an emitter-follower series regulator and provides an output which is within a few tenths of a volt of the reference voltage of 12-volt battery B1. Q3 also provides further filtering, making the voltage to the load essentially free of ripple. Switch S1B, which is part of the power switch, disconnects B1 from the circuit when the supply is not used. Without R3 in the circuit, some current is drawn from the battery—approximately the load current divided by the collector-to-base current gain of Q3. For example, if the load current were 0.5 ampere and the gain were 20, the battery would supply about 25 milliamperes.

With R3 out of the circuit the output is free of ripple. With R3 in the circuit the battery current may be brought to zero or even reversed to charged the battery, thus making the life of the battery in the circuit the same as its shelf life. This may, however, introduce a slight amount of ripple into the output, depending on the internal impedance of the battery and the value of R3 used. If the internal impedance of the battery were zero, then the presence of R3 would have no effect. The proper value of R3 may be determined by measuring the current in B1 with the desired load on the power supply and inserting values of R3 to make the battery current zero or slightly reversed. Or, R3 may be a 47-ohm resistor in series with a 250-ohm potentiometer. The ripple introduced depends on the amount of battery current to be balanced out (which is also dependent on load current) and the internal resistance of the battery; it probably will not exceed a few tenths of a millivolt at a ½-ampere load.

PORTABLE SCR AND SILICON RECTIFIER TESTER

This circuit is a simple portable tester for silicon-controlled rectifiers (SCR's) and silicon-diode rectifiers. While not as sophisticated as those used for precise laboratory work and semiconductor comparative evaluation, its straightforward GO/NO GO operation is ideal for many types of general troubleshooting and service work. The test set detects opens and shorts in diode rectifiers and SCR's. In addition, it also checks forward blocking ability and triggering on SCR's. Convenient battery operation is particularly useful when working with automotive, marine, and aircraft equipment. This tester is more objective than the often used ohmmeter type of test because it applies at least 10 volts to the semiconductor under test. Satisfactory condition of the semiconductor parameter being tested is indicated by a lamp. Failure of the lamp to light denotes a defective semiconductor for the specific test conditions.

Controlled rectifier SCR1, which has a sensitive-gate-triggering characteristic and acts as a high-gain amplifier, compares the signal from the parameter being tested against its critical gate-triggering voltage and energizes the lamp if the parameter is satisfactory. Separate batteries energize the measuring and indicating circuits. A five-position rotary switch permits easy consecutive selection of the individual tests; battery check, forward voltage drop and gate trigger, reverse-leakage current, forward-leakage current, and off.

When the rotary switch is placed in the battery-check position, the gate of SCR1 measures a small portion of the voltage

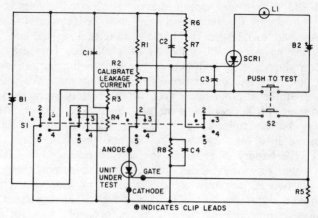

PARTS LIST

R1 — 22K, 1W
R2 — 1000 OHM POTENTIOMETER
R3, R4 — 4.7K, 1W
R5 — 1K, 1W
R6 — 680 OHMS, 1W
R7, R8 — 100K, 1W
C1, C4 — .01 MFD
C2, C3 — .1 MFD
S1 — 4 POLE, 5 POSITION, NON-SHORTING ROTARY SWITCH

S2 — 2 POLE, N.O. PUSHBUTTON, BOTTOM CONTACT ADJUSTED AS INDICATED IN TEXT.

B1 — 67-½ VOLT DRY CELL
B2 — 3 VOLT DRY CELL
L1 — G.E. #49 LIGHT BULB
SCR1 — G.E. C5U CONTROLLED RECTIFIER

ROTARY SWITCH POSITIONS

1 BATTERY CHECK
2 FORWARD VOLTAGE DROP AND GATE TRIGGER (FOR SCR'S)
3 REVERSE LEAKAGE CURRENT
4 FORWARD LEAKAGE CURRENT (FOR SCR'S ONLY)
5 OFF

(A) Complete schematic.

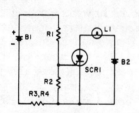

(B) Battery-check mode.

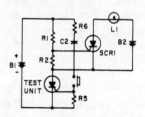

(C) Forward-voltage drop and gate-trigger mode.

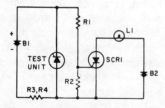

(D) Reverse-leakage–current mode.

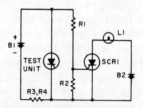

(E) Forward-leakage–current mode.

Courtesy of General Electric Co.

Portable SCR and silicon-rectifier tester circuits.

170

of measuring battery B1. If the battery voltage is too low, SCR1 fails to fire and therefore does not light the indicating lamp. If indicating-lamp battery B2 is discharged too far, the lamp also fails to light.

When the rotary switch is placed in the forward voltage-drop test position, the diode or SCR under test is placed in series with the measuring circuit and a gate signal is applied if the semiconductor is an SCR. Provided the forward voltage drop of the unit under test is satisfactorily low, SCR1 will trigger and light the indicating lamp.

When the rotary switch is placed in the reverse-leakage–current position, the diode or SCR under test is placed in parallel with the resistance divider of the detecting circuit. Excessive leakage current diverts current from sensing resistor R2, thereby preventing SCR1 from triggering and the lamp from lighting. In the forward leakage-current test position (for SCR's only) the SCR under test is again placed across the sensing circuit with its cathode and anode reversed. Operation is the same as in the reverse leakage-current test.

In position 2 (forward voltage-drop and gate-trigger test) push button S2 triggers the gate of the SCR under test when it is depressed, and resets SCR1 when it is released between tests. For proper operation, the contacts should be adjusted so that the top contact (in the indicating lamp circuit) closes slightly before the lower contact (in the gate circuit).

CHOPPER-CONTROLLED, REGULATED POWER SUPPLY

This circuit is capable of operating directly from a DC line or from an AC supply through use of a rectifier and rough filter as shown on the diagram. This circuit has several advantages, such as being capable of operating in a stable condition over a wide range of the AC input frequency. Because the chopping circuit operates in the 500- to 2,000-cps range this circuit also has inherently faster response than a phase-controlled circuit operating at normal line frequencies. Filter requirements are less, and the AC supply sees essentially a unity power-factor load with little distortion effect on the line voltage as compared to phase-controlled circuits.

When controlled rectifier SCR1 is fired by a gate pulse from transformer T2, power is delivered to the load, and the auto-transformer action of T1 causes capacitor C4 to become charged with its bottom plate positive with respect to its top plate. When T1 saturates, the voltage on C4 is applied to the cathode of SCR1, switching it off. However, current continues to flow through the

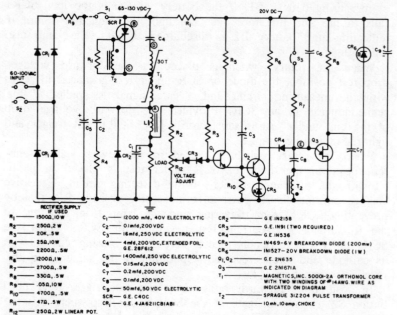

RECTIFIER SUPPLY IF USED						
R_1	1500Ω,10 W	C_1	12000 mfd, 40V ELECTROLYTIC	CR_2	G.E. IN2158	
R_2	250Ω,2 W	C_2	0.1mfd,200 VDC	CR_3	G.E. IN91 (TWO REQUIRED)	
R_3	20K,.5W	C_3	16mfd,250 VDC ELECTROLYTIC	CR_4	G.E. IN536	
R_4	25Ω,10W	C_4	4mfd,200 VDC,EXTENDED FOIL, G.E. 28F612	CR_5	IN469-6 V BREAKDOWN DIODE (200mw)	
R_5	2200Ω,.5W			CR_6	IN1527- 20V BREAKDOWN DIODE (1 W)	
R_6	1200Ω,1 W	C_5	1400mfd,250 VDC ELECTROLYTIC	Q_1,Q_2	G.E. 2N635	
R_7	2700Ω,.5W	C_6	0.15mfd,200 VDC	Q_3	G.E 2NI671A	
R_8	330Ω,.5 W	C_7	0.2mfd,200 VDC	T_1	MAGNETICS,INC. 5000I-2A ORTHONOL CORE WITH TWO WINDINGS OF #14AWG WIRE AS INDICATED ON DIAGRAM	
R_9	.05Ω,10W	C_8	0.1mfd,200 VDC			
R_{10}	4700Ω,.5W	C_9	50mfd,50 VDC ELECTROLYTIC	T_2	SPRAGUE 3IZ204 PULSE TRANSFORMER	
R_{11}	47Ω,.5 W	SCR	G.E. C40C	L	10 mh, 10 amp CHOKE	
R_{12}	250Ω,2 W LINEAR POT.	CR_1	G.E. 4JA62IICBIABI			

Courtesy of General Electric Co.

Circuit of chopper-controlled, regulated power supply.

load and diode CR2 due to the inductive effect of choke L1 and through the load due to the energy stored in C1. The feedback control of the output voltage relies on unijunction-transistor relaxation oscillator Q3 to develop firing pulses for the gate of SCR1. These pulses are coupled to the gate through T2.

With the voltage adjust potentiometer (R12) at its bottom position, no feedback signal is present. Under these conditions the UJT oscillates at its maximum rate, approximately 2 kc, and maximum voltage is applied to the load. As the arm of R12 is moved up so that its portion of the load voltage exceeds the reference voltage of CR5, Q2 starts to conduct, and part of the current flowing down through R7 is diverted from C8 through CR4 and the collector of Q2. C8 then takes longer to charge to the peak-point voltage of Q3, and the repetition rate of the UJT oscillator and SCR decreases. Load voltage is also decreased. For a given setting of R12, so that the load voltage is at or near the design objective of 28 volts, the feedback circuit will regulate the repetition rate so as to maintain load voltage constant with variations in supply voltage and load current. The two diodes (CR3) compensate for temperature variations in the base-to-emitter voltage drop of Q1 and Q2. Resistor R9 is a surge resistor designed to protect CR1 against excessive inrush current to C5.

CASCADE-AMPLIFIER REGULATOR

The cascade-amplifier regulator provides a regulated, variable DC output between zero and 12 volts from a 105- to 130-volt AC input. The 115-volt AC input is applied to the 15-volt zener supply. The 15-volt DC output is used as a bias

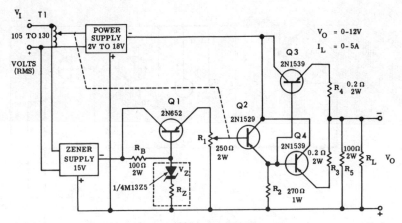

Courtesy of Motorola Semiconductor Products, Inc.
Circuit of cascade-amplifier regulator.

voltage for series-regulator transistor Q1. The base bias is fixed by the zener diode. The resulting regulated current through variable resistor R1 provides a reference voltage for the regulator circuit. A portion of the supply voltage is taken from auto transformer T1 and applied to the variable 2- to 18-volt power supply. The output of the variable power supply is used for bias voltages on transistors Q2, Q3, and Q4.

The setting of variable resistor R1 determines the base bias on Q2 and thus the voltage output of the regulator. The conduction level of Q2 determines the current through emitter resistor R2, controlling the current through series regulators Q3 and Q4. The output series regulators are paralleled to permit large load currents without exceeding the transistor power rating. It is necessary to carefully match parallel transistors or to use a small resistor in series with each emitter, thus equalizing the emitter currents. Bleeder resistors R2 and R5 maintain regulation at very low load currents. If these are not used at some minimum load current the zener will no longer control the unit ter voltages of transistors Q2, Q3, and Q4, and the output voltage will float up to the power-supply voltage.

1000-WATT REGULATED SUPPLY

The 1,000-watt supply is controlled by a 10-watt zener diode. This supply is designed to deliver 0 to 35 amperes at a nominal 28 volts DC with expected AC line variation of 105 to 125 volts. The line voltage is stepped down by transformer T1 and rectified by bridge recti-

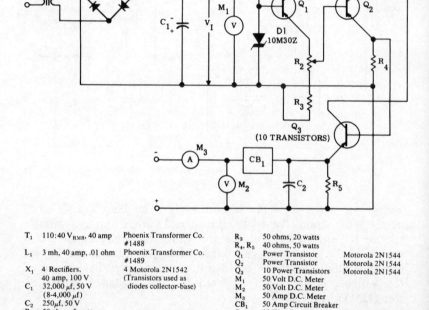

T_1	110:40 V_{RMS}, 40 amp	Phoenix Transformer Co. #1488	R_3	50 ohms, 20 watts	
L_1	3 mh, 40 amp, .01 ohm	Phoenix Transformer Co. #1489	R_4, R_5	40 ohms, 50 watts	
			Q_1	Power Transistor	Motorola 2N1544
X_1	4 Rectifiers, 40 amp, 100 V	4 Motorola 2N1542 (Transistors used as	Q_2	Power Transistor	Motorola 2N1544
C_1	32,000 μf, 50 V	diodes collector-base)	Q_3	10 Power Transistors	Motorola 2N1544
	(8-4,000 μf)		M_1	50 Volt D.C. Meter	
C_2	250μf, 50 V		M_2	50 Volt D.C. Meter	
R_1	50 ohms, 5 watts		M_3	50 Amp D.C. Meter	
R_2	12 ohms, 10 watts		CB_1	50 Amp Circuit Breaker	
			Z	10 Watt Zener Diode	Motorola 10M30Z5

Courtesy of Motorola Semiconductor Products, Inc.
Circuit of 1,000-watt regulated supply.

fier X1. The rectified output is filtered by inductor L1 and capacitor C1. Zener diode D1 provides a steady voltage at the base of transisto. Q1. This constant base voltage results in a constant level of conduction through Q1, R2, and R3. The voltage developed across R3 and variable resistor R2 is applied to the base of voltage-regulator transistor Q2.

This adjustable, regulated base voltage controls the voltage output of the regulated supply. The voltage developed at the emitter of Q2 is applied to the bases of ten parallel-connected, series-regulator transistors (Q3). The ten paralleled transistors are needed to carry the high output current of the power supply. Bleeder resistor R5 maintains regulation at very low load currents. If this is not used, at some minimum load current the zener will no longer control the emitter voltages of transistors Q2 and Q3, and the output voltage will approach the supply voltage. Capacitor C2 provides additional filtering of the output voltage. Circuit breaker CB1 is in the circuit to protect the output transistors from excessive current. Meters M1, M2, and M3 provide visual monitoring of the power-supply voltage, load voltage, and load current, respectively.

150-WATT REGULATED SUPPLY

This 150-watt, regulated supply uses a 6.8-volt zener diode to regulate the output voltage over a range of 0 to 30 volts. A portion of the source voltage is coupled through autotransformer T1 and isolation transformer T2 to full-wave bridge rectifier X1. The rectified output from X1 is filtered by inductor L1 and capacitor C1. In a similar manner the line voltage is coupled through transformer T3 and rectified by full-wave rectifier X2. The rectified output from X2 is filtered by resistor R11 and capacitor C5. Bias for the base of control transistor Q1 is taken from the junction of resistors R5 and R6. Potentiometer R5 is ganged to the variable autotransformer so that as the voltage from the autotransformer increases, the resistance of R5 also increases, keeping the voltage drop across sensing resistor R6 nearly constant. By this means the collector current of control transistor Q1 is held constant.

The zener diode maintains a stable reference voltage for comparison with the voltage developed across R6. Transistors Q2 and Q3 are current amplifiers for series regulator Q4 through Q11. Thermistor R7 compensates for temperature-variation effects on zener-diode voltage and control transistor Q1. Bridge rectifier X2 is the DC voltage supply for the zener diode. This separate power supply is necessary to limit current variations through the zener diode to small changes caused by line-voltage fluctuations. This supply should be sufficient to furnish the required zener current plus the no-load emitter current of Q4 through Q11. For good zener voltage regulation, zener current should never be less than 10% of the emitter current of Q4 through Q11. Current-feedback resistor R2 is included in the circuit to improve the load regulation. Voltage feedback resistor R8, which is a 3-2-volt, 3J0-ma light bulb, improves the line-voltage regulation.

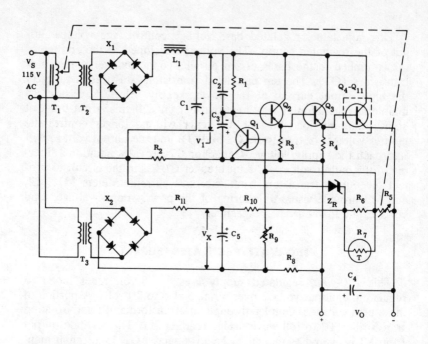

T_1 Powerstat type 20 Superior Electric - 3 Ampere	C_4 1000μf -- 50V	R_4 100Ω 10W
	C_5 1000μfd -- 50V	R_5 400Ω potentiometer 4W
T_2 UTC H-96 115V -- 40V, 6A	Z_R 10M6.8Z Motorola	R_6 70Ω, 1/2W
T_3 Triad F25X 12.6V, 1.5A, filament transformer	Q_1 2N1540 Motorola	R_7 RB38L1 Thermistor -- Fenwal Elec.
X_1 4 -- 1N253 Motorola	Q_2, Q_3 2N1539 Motorola	R_8 #45 GE light bulb, 3.2V, 350 ma
X_2 4 -- 1N1563 Motorola	Q_4-Q_{11} 8 - 2N1539 Motorola	R_9 1500Ω Potentiometer
C_1 12000μfd - 50V	R_1 100Ω 1W	R_{10} 5Ω, 1W
C_2 4000μfd -- 50V	R_2 9.5 inches of #22 copper wire	R_{11} 5Ω, 5W
C_3 4000μfd -- 50V	R_3 100Ω 10W	L_1 Triad F18A 6.3V, 6A, filament transformer

Courtesy of Motorola Semiconductor Products, Inc.

Circuit of 150-watt regulated supply.

SIMPLE, ZENER-DIODE VOLTAGE REGULATORS

Circuit A shows a transformerless, 10-volt power supply that is regulated to better than ±5% against nominal variations in both line supply and load current. The regulated supply uses half-wave rectifier diode D1 with an incandescent bulb as a ballast to rectify the 110-volt AC line voltage. Zener diode D2 is connected across the output and prevents the rectified voltage from exceeding 10 volts. Capacitor C1 filters the rectified voltage by shorting any AC component in the rectified output. The use of an incandescent bulb as a ballast provides not only economy, convenience, and safety, but also a wide range of currents in the many wattage ratings available. An important feature

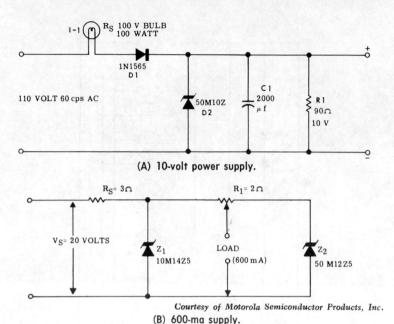

(B) 600-ma supply.

Circuits of zener-diode voltage regulators.

of the incandescent bulb ballast is that the volt-ampere characteristic tends to maintain constant current, and, in turn, aid the regulation.

Circuit B shows a supply that is relatively unaffected by load, is adjustable, and provides a regulated reference or power source. For precise output-voltage control, the voltage levels of zener diodes Z1 and Z2 can be selected quite close together; the difference will appear across R1. Resistor R1 is adjustable, thus providing a variable output voltage. With the constants shown, regulation is better than $\pm3\%$ for all settings of R1 and load currents up to 600 ma.

CURRENT REGULATOR

This circuit shows a current regulator for handling from 1 to 10 amperes at 50 volts DC. It has a power capability of 450 watts with an efficiency of 90%. Regulation at 10 amperes with load changes from 0 ohms to 4.5 ohms is about 2%.

This DC regulator uses five paralleled power transistors (type 2N 575) as the series element driven by a 2N1659 transistor. Potentiometer R2 provides an adjustable reference voltage, permitting the output current to be set for any level from 1 to 10 amperes.

Series resistor R1 provides an error signal through transistor Q6, maintaining a constant preset current level as the load conditions vary.

177

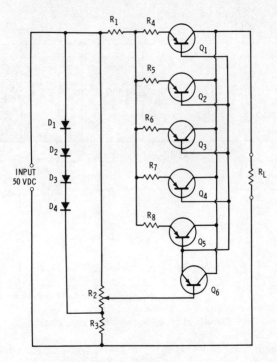

Q$_1$ thru Q$_5$ = Minneapolis-Honeywell 2N575
Q$_6$ = Minneapolis-Honeywell 2N1659
D$_1$ thru D$_4$ = 1N1217 (or equivalent)
R$_L$ = 0 to 50 ohms (determined in part by load current)
R$_1$ = 0.1 ohms, 10 watts, Resistor
R$_2$ = 100 ohms, 2 watts Potentiometer
R$_3$ = 1.5 K ohms, 2 watts, Resistor
R$_4$ thru R$_8$ = 0.2 ohms, 1 watt
    Resistor

Courtesy of Minneapolis-Honeywell Regulator Co.
Current-regulator circuit.

SERIES VOLTAGE REGULATOR

This circuit demonstrates the use of power transistors in a series type of voltage-regulator circuit. The input voltage is 86 volts ±15%, and the regulated output voltage is 70 volts. The load current can vary from 0 to 4 amperes and the regulation from no load to full load is 2.5%. The ripple rejection of this circuit is 40 db. As in other types of series voltage-regulator circuits, the drop across the series elements varies in order to keep the output voltage constant.

The base of Q4, a 2N1482 medium-power silicon transistor, has a reference voltage established through the use of diode CR1. A voltage taken from control R7 is fed to the base of Q5. These transistors together form a differential amplifier, the output of which indicates whether the regulated voltage is going up or down. The output of this circuit is used to control the series-regulator transistors.

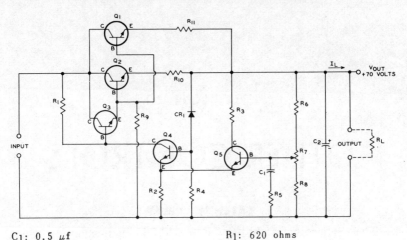

C_1: 0.5 μf

C_2: 25 μf, 100 v

CR_1: 1N1363-R silicon reference diode

Q_1, Q_2: RCA-2N1489 high-power silicon transistors

Q_3: RCA-2N1485 intermediate-power silicon transistor

Q_4, Q_5: RCA-2N1482 medium-power silicon transistors

R_1: 620 ohms

R_2: 1000 ohms

R_3: 750 ohms

R_4: 4000 ohms

R_5: 100 ohms

R_6: 2500 ohms

R_7: Potentiometer, 1000 ohms

R_8: 3500 ohms

R_9: 20000 ohms

R_{10}, R_{11}: 0.5 ohm

Courtesy of Radio Corporation of America.

Series-voltage—regulator circuit.

OTHER CONTROLS

LATCHING RELAY

This circuit shows the use of a 2N1303 germanium switching transistor together with a No. 49 light bulb and a cadmium sulphide cell to provide a simple latching-relay circuit. There are two inputs as

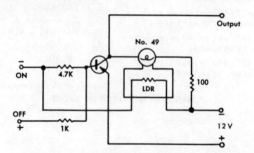

Courtesy Ferroxcube Corporation of America.
Latching-relay circuit.

shown; one to turn the circuit on, and the other to turn it off. As indicated, this circuit is for 12 volts DC. However, it can operate on other voltages depending on the particular transistor that is used.

In this circuit a small base current causes the lamp to barely glow. This glow lowers the resistance of the light-dependent resistor (LDR), or cadmium photocell, and this increases the base current, which increases the current flow through the lamp, hence the intensity of the light. This is a regenerative type of action that increases to the maximum value once it has been started. Note that only a small initial signal is required at the base, and this initial "on" signal, or trigger, is amplified by the transistor circuit to produce the switching action. In order to turn the circuit off, a positive voltage is required at the "off" terminal.

FIRE ALARM

This is a single transistor used as a fire-alarm circuit. As with a remote-temperature indicator, the current flow through the transistor is a function of temperature. At normal room temperature the transistor is biased so that there is a small amount of current flow. As the transis-

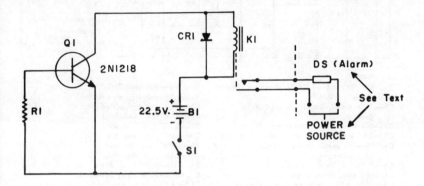

B1—22 ½V. Battery, Burgess #5156SC or equivalent.
DS—Bell, Buzzer or Light (See text).
*K1—Relay, Potter & Brumfield, SM5DS, 900Ω 18V. D.C.,
(fits 7 pin. min. tube socket) or equivalent.
CR1—Sylvania 1N34A Diode.
Q1—Sylvania 2N1218 Transistor.
R1—10K ½w. Resistor.
S1—S.P.S.T. Toggle Switch.

*The SM5DS relay has contacts rated at 2 amperes for non inductive load. If heavier current is required operate a heavy duty relay from the contacts of the SM5DS.

Courtesy of Sylvania Electric Products, Inc.
Fire-alarm circuit.

tor is heated, leakage current through the transistor increases the current flow through the relay coil until the relay contacts are closed. This circuit with the component values shown can be tested by applying a lighted match to the transistor itself. A few moments after the heat is applied, the current flow increases to the point where the relay closes.

The relay contacts are closed to complete a separate external circuit. This external circuit has an alarm and power source in series. The power source and the alarm can be arranged in any manner depending on the specific needs. For example, a separate AC source can

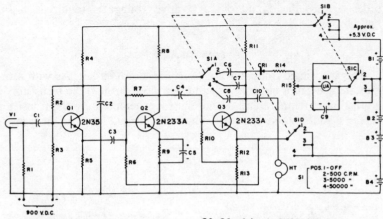

B1, B2, B3, B4—1.345V. Mercury Battery Mallory RM-4R.
C1—500 mmfd. Capacitor, 1600V. or greater.
C2—0.1 mfd. Paper Capacitor.
C3—330 mmfd. Ceramic or Mica Capacitor.
C4, C5—25 mfd. Electrolytic Capacitor, 6V or greater.
C6—0.5 mfd. Paper Capacitor.
C7—.05 mfd. Paper Capacitor.
C8—.005 mfd. Paper or Mica Capacitor.
C9—300 mfd. Electrolytic Capacitor, 3V. or greater.
C10—.01 mfd. Paper Capacitor.
CR1—Sylvania Silicon Diode 1N456.
HT—Earphones, approximately 2000 ohms.
M1—Meter, 0 to 50 microamperes D.C.
Q1—Sylvania 2N35 Transistor.

Q2, Q3—Sylvania 2N233A Transistor.
R1—1 megohm ½ w. Resistor.
R2—100K ½ w. Resistor.
R3—47K ½ w. Resistor.
R4—6.3K ½ w. Resistor.
R5—10K ½ w. Resistor.
R6—3.9K ½ w. Resistor.
R7—22K ½ w. Resistor.
R8, R11—3.3K ½ w. Resistor.
R9, R10—2.2K ½ w. Resistor.
R12—470Ω ½ w. Resistor.
R13, R14—1000Ω ½ w. Resistor.
R15—2500Ω Potentiometer.
S1—Rotary Wafer Switch, 4 poles 4 position, or more positions used with a stop.
V1—Geiger Tube, Victoreen 1B85 or Tracerlab TGC-6.

(A) Radiation-detector circuit.

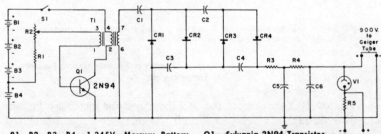

B1, B2, B3, B4—1.345V. Mercury Battery, Mallory RM-4R.
C1, C2, C3, C4—.01 Mfd. 500V. Disc Ceramic Capacitor.
C5, C6—.01 Mfd. 2000V. Disc Ceramic Capacitor.
CR1, CR2, CR3, CR4—Sylvania 1N2071 Rectifier.

Q1—Sylvania 2N94 Transistor.
R1—3.3K ½ w. Resistor.
R2—25K Potentiometer.
R3, R4—4.7 Megohm ½ w. Resistor.
R5—100K ½ w. Resistor.
S1—S.P.S.T. Toggle Switch.
T1—Transformer, U.T.C. Type 0-3 Ouncer.
V1—Corona Regulator Tube, Victoreen 5841.

(B) 900-volt power supply.

Courtesy of Sylvania Electric Products, Inc.

Circuit for Geiger-tube radiation detector.

be used together with an alarm such as a bell or flashing light, or a battery-operated alarm can be used.

GEIGER-TUBE RADIATION DETECTOR

A Geiger-tube counter is a radiation detector used in prospecting for uranium or other types of radioactive ore. This is a three transistor unit feeding a pair of earphones and driven by a Geiger-counter tube. The meter that is used to visually indicate the counts will show a normal background of about 50 counts per minute.

The Geiger tube that actually detects the radiation is powered by a 900-volt DC supply. This supply can be 3 individual 300-volt batteries in series or a transistor-blocking–oscillator type of power supply in which the blocking oscillator generates an alternating current that is stepped up and rectified. (Circuit B).

The first transistor (Q1) is an emitter-follower designed to match the high impedance of the Geiger tube to the rest of the circuit. The remaining two transistors (Q2 and Q3) together form a multivibrator driven by the amplified Geiger-counter pulses. Q2 is normally conducting, and Q3 is normally cut off. The negative pulse from the Geiger tube switches the multivibrator to the other state. In this circuit, the range switch varies the time constant in the multivibrator circuit. This determines the meter current per pulse. Position 2 is for up to 500 counts per minute, position 3 is for up to 5,000 counts per minute, and position 4 is for up to 50,000 counts per minute. The control, R15, in the collector circuit of Q3, is usually adjusted to give a full count of 5,000 counts per minute in the range position 3. The diode, CR1, is used to prevent current flow through the meter except when an input pulse from the Geiger tube occurs.

SOUND-OPERATED RELAY

Audio signals such as an automobile horn or a voice can operate this relay circuit. For a horn, the circuit can be arranged to open a garage door or turn on lights when the automobile horn is sounded. A voice can also operate this relay to turn on an intercom or other devcie.

Two stages provide the required gain, and Q3 is the relay driver. Audio modulates the DC current flowing through the carbon microphone. The signal is amplified by Q1, a grounded-emitter stage utilizing transformer coupling. The signal is amplified further by Q2, another grounded-emitter stage.

The output signal from Q2 is changed to DC by the positive half-wave rectifier. This positive DC voltage is applied to the base of Q3, which in turn makes Q3 conduct enough current to actuate Relay K1 The sound level at which the relay will close can be adjusted by varying R7.

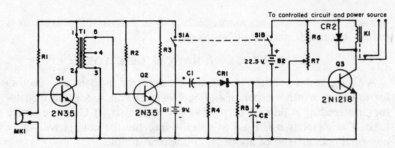

To controlled circuit and power source

B1 9V. Battery, Burgess #2N6 with snap terminals or equivalent.

B2—22½V. Battery, Burgess #5156SC or equivalent.

C1—5 Mfd. Electrolytic Capacitor, 25V. or greater.

C2—50 Mfd. Electrolytic Capacitor, 30V or greater.

CR1—Sylvania 1N456 Diode.

CR2—Sylvania 1N34A Diode.

*K1—Relay, Potter & Brumfield, SM5DS, 900Ω, 18V. DC., (fits 7 pin min. tube socket) or equivalent.

MK1—Microphone, single button carbon.

Q1, Q2—Sylvania 2N35 Transistor.

Q3—Sylvania 2N1218 Transistor.

R1—3K ½w. Resistor.

R2—15K ½w. Resistor.

R3—820Ω ½w. Resistor.

R4—10K ½w. Resistor.

R5—100K ½w. Resistor.

R6—4.7K ½w. Resistor.

R7—10K Potentiometer.

S1—D.P.S.T. Toggle Switch.

T1—Transformer Triad TZ-15.

*The SM5DS relay has contacts rated at 2 amperes, for non inductive load. If heavier current is required operate a heavy duty relay from the contacts of the SM5DS.

Courtesy of Sylvania Electric Products, Inc.

Circuit for sound-operated relay.

LEAD-SULFIDE, PHOTOCONDUCTOR RADIATION-DETECTOR CIRCUIT

There are many types of photo-conductor detectors. This circuit shows the lead sulfide detector (*Ektron*) produced by Eastman Kodak. There are various types of units available, and their useful range extends from about 0.25 microns (2,500 Angstroms) to 3.5 microns (35,000 Angstroms). Their resistance is a function of the light or radiation intensity; hence they can be used in detector circuits. A typical detector circuit is shown.

Because this unit has an excellent spectral response and a good signal-to-noise ratio, it can be used for many applications where other photoconductor cells cannot be used. In this particular circuit, an auxiliary amplifier is shown so that there will be an operation of the electrical switch in the event of a small and relatively abrupt change in the amount of radiation falling on the detector. Thus the device can be used to control electrical power to devices such as alarm bells or motors.

As shown, a single transformer is used in the power supply, and any transformer whose primary will take 117 volts AC and convert it to 6.3 volts AC may be used in the circuit. After rectification, the 150 volts DC is the plate supply of the 2D21 thyratron. The 6.3 volts AC secondary provides the filament power for the thyratron. A bias voltage from the power supply cuts off the thyratron when no light falls on the detector. When light falls on the detecting element, the grid voltage is increased above the firing value, causing the thyratron to fire. This in turn closes the relay. As in other circuits of this general type, the thyratron is triggered into operation and carries the full current the moment the grid rises to the conduction voltage. Note that capacitive coupling is used between the control grid and the detector so that triggering will occur only on abrupt changes in radiation.

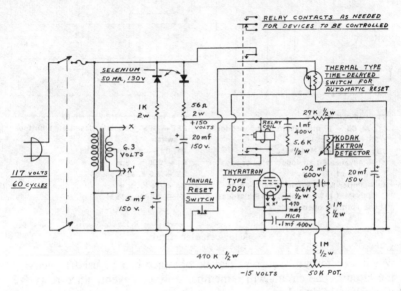

Photoconductor radiation-detector circuit.

In this circuit, when the relay operates, the thyratron is almost immediately turned off, and the relay is locked in the energized position since there is a set of contacts on the relay which remove the plate voltage from the thyratron and at the same time maintain current flow to the relay coil. Reset is accomplished by the manual reset button or an appropriate thermal time-delay switch. A control is shown for the manual adjustment of the trigger level for the thyratron, which determines its point of conduction. In some applications it is possible to replace this control by a fixed resistor of an appropriate value after testing the circuit parameters for the desired levels. It is also possible to operate this circuit using direct current such as a 90-volt battery; in this case a dropping resistor is needed for the thyratron filament.

185

RELAY ACTUATOR

The relay actuator is a one-event memory circuit requiring an actuating voltage as low as 3 mv. The relay actuator is extremely useful in registering things such as whether or not the phone rang while the owner was away, whether or not lights were turned on, if doors were opened or doorbells rung, and so on. Practically any event from

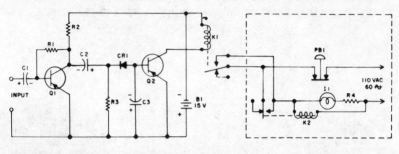

B1 — 15-volt battery

C1, C2, C3 — 10 mfd electrolytic capacitor, 25 v

CR1 — Sylvania 1N34A diode

K1 — Advance SO 1C 4000D relay or equivalent

K2 — Potter & Brumfield Type CA3A or equivalent 110 vac relay, having at least one normally open contact

I1 — neon lamp; NE-2 or NE-51

PBI — SPST normally closed push-button switch

Q1, Q2 — Sylvania 2N1265

R1 — 330 k, ½ w

R2 — 6.8 k, ½ w

R3 — 15 k, ½ w

R4 — 1.5 meg, ½ w

Courtesy of Sylvania Electric Products, Inc.

Relay-actuator circuit.

which an alternating current can be obtained can be used to activate the circuit. The circuit will remember only one event, since relay K2 is a self-holding relay.

Any AC input above 3 mv rms, and between ½ cps and 1 mc operates the circuit. The input signal is coupled through capacitor C1 to the base of grounded-emitter, AC-amplifier transistor Q1. Resistor R1 provides the base bias. Resistor R2 is the collector load resistor for Q1. The amplified signal from the collector of Q1 is coupled through capacitor C2 to a detector network consisting of diode CR1, resistor R3, and capacitor C3. The negative detected signal from the junction of CR1 and C3 is applied to the base of transistor Q2. This negative voltage drives Q2 into conduction. When Q2 is driven into conduction, collector current flows through the coil of relay K1, energizing K1. When K1 is energized, 110 volts AC is applied across the coil of relay K2, energizing K2. Neon lamp I1 provides visual indication that K2 has been energized. Resistor R4 is a current limiting resistor for I1. When the input signal is removed from the relay actuator, relay K1 is de-energized. However, the 110 volts AC is now applied through the holding contacts of K2 to the coil, holding K2 energized. Relay K2 will remain energized providing indication that a signal has been applied to the input of the relay actuator. In order to de-energize K2, push-button switch PB1 must be depressed, removing the 110 volts AC from the coil of K2. If input voltages larger than ½ volt rms are to be used, an input attenuator should be used.

AUTOMATIC GARAGE LIGHT

This circuit automatically turns on the garage lights when the detector is illuminated by the auto headlamps. After the headlamps have been turned off, it holds the garage lights on for 1½ to 20 minutes, allowing the driver sufficient time to enter the house.

The heart of the automatic garage light is the energy-storage

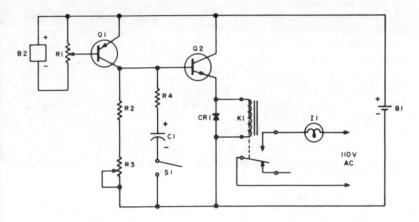

B1 — 15-volt battery
B2 — Sun battery, International Rectifier
   Corp., Type B2M or equivalent
C1 — 1000 mfd electrolytic, 15-volt
CR1 — Sylvania 1N34 diode
I1 — 115-volt light bulb, wattage not greater
   than 100
K1 — 1 kohm sensitive relay, Sigma
   11F-1000G or equivalent

Q1 — Sylvania 2N1265 transistor
Q2 — Sylvania 2N229 transistor
R1 — 10 k potentiometer
R2 — 22 k, ½ w
R3 — 1 meg potentiometer
R4 — 1 k, ½ w
S1 — Single-pole, single-throw switch;
   slide, toggle, or push button

Courtesy of Sylvania Electric Products, Inc.

Circuit for automatic garage light.

capacitor (C1). When the auto headlamps strike the sun battery (B2), a bias current is generated for transistor Q1. This produces a bias on Q2. This lowers the collector impedance, providing a charge path for capacitor C1. Resistor R4 limits the surge charging current of C1. Adjustment of potentiometer R1 varies the sensitivity so that the charging action occurs at the desired level of illumination. When the illumination is removed from B2, the conduction in Ql decreases markedly, increasing the output impedance. Capacitor C1 now discharges through R4 and the parallel paths of the output impedance of Q1, the input impedance of Q2, and resistors R2 and R3. Since the output impedance of Q1 is very high, and the input impedance of emitter-follower Q2 is also very high, the main discharge path for C1 is through R2, R3, and R4. The setting of R3 determines the discharge time of C1. Resistor R3 can be adjusted for a discharge time ranging from 1½ to 15 minutes. Removal of R2 and R3 results in a discharge time of approximately 20 minutes. The emitter-follower action of Q2 drives relay K1 with a voltage that resembles the exponentially-discharging capacitor voltage. Diode CR1 damps the voltage spikes generated by the relay coil when the drive voltage is suddenly withdrawn. The current through the coil of K1 energizes K1, applying 110 volts to the garage light.

When switch S1 is open, the large time constant is removed from the circuit and R1 may be rapidly adjusted. As the control is advanced, the relay closes when the sun battery is illuminated. As it is further advanced, a point is reached at which the relay will no longer open for ambient light. Resistor R1 should be set just below this point so that the relay opens for the brightest ambient light that is expected. Now, close S1 and the automatic garage light is ready to operate.

If the garage light is to be larger than 100 watts, it is desirable to use a second relay operating directly on the 115-volt line to prevent burning of the realy contacts. It may also be necessary to shield the sun battery to prevent it from locking-up on the garage light that it turns on.

RAIN-ALARM CIRCUIT

The rain alarm circuit indicates the presence of rain. When rain drops fall across the rain probes, the alarm circuit is energized. Instead of using an indicator lamp as shown in this circuit, you could use an alarm system such as a buzzer, or you could use an intermediate relay to activate a number of mechanisms such as a device for closing windows when it starts to rain.

The rain probe is easily constructed by supporting two bare conductors so that they run parallel to each other approximately 1/16th of an inch apart. Any gauge wire may be used for the probes, providing they are stiff enough to maintain their shape. A two-inch length is adequate. Several probes may be connected in parrallel; all of them are connected to one circuit. In this case, they should be placed in several strategic locations to catch the rain drops. The rain probes should be slightly elevated above nearby surfaces, since surface contamination can produce an impedance low enough to trip the circuit.

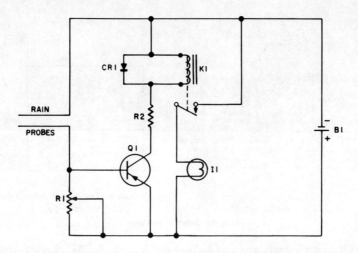

B1 — 12-volt battery	K1 — 1 kohm sensitive relay
CR1 — Sylvania 1N34A diode	(Sigma 11F-1000G or equivalent)
I1 — 12-volt indicator lamp	Q1 — Sylvania 2N1265 transistor
	R1 — 5 k, ½ w potentiometer
	R2 — 220 Ω, 1 w

Courtesy of Sylvania Electric Products, Inc.

Rain-alarm circuit.

When a rain drop falls across the rain probes, a small current flows through transistor Q1. The small current is amplified by Q1 and applied to the coil of relay K1. Resistor R1 is a shunt across the control junction of the transistor. If its value is low, a large part of the current flowing through the drop of rain will flow through R1 instead of through the transistor. Therefore, decreasing the value of R1 will decrease the sensitivity of the circuit. Resistor R2 is a current limiting resistor protecting Q1 from excessive current. Diode CR1, connected across the coil of relay K1, shorts the high voltage spikes generated by the inductance of K1 when the transistor cuts off. When relay K1 is energized, the battery voltage from B1 is applied across the indicator lamp I1 or to whatever alarm circuit is used.

LAMP-DIMMER CIRCUITS

Full-wave lamp-dimmer circuit A gives smooth lamp brilliance control over the full range of brightness-control potentiometer R2. The dimmer circuit consists of two controlled rectifiers connected back to back.

When voltage is applied to the circuit, capacitor C1 charges through resistor R2, diode D2, and resistor R1. At the same time capacitor C2 charges through resistor R3, diode D3, and resistor R1. When capaci-

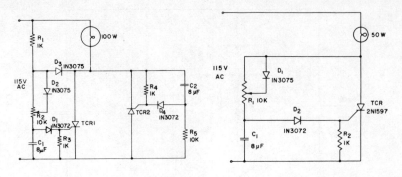

Courtesy of Transitron Electronic Corp.

(A) Full-wave circuit.   (B) Half-wave circuit.

Lamp-dimmer circuits.

tor C1 is sufficiently charged to forward-bias diode D1, current flows
through resistor R3 and diode D1, providing a gating voltage for controlled rectifier TCR1. The setting of brightness-control potentiometer
R2 determines the charge time of capacitor C1, thus determining the
conduction time of TCR1. When TCR1 has a short conduction time,
capacitor C2 charges to a negative voltage during the major part of a
half cycle, and it will take a major part of the next half cycle to build
up the positive voltage at C2 to the level necessary to fire controlled
rectifier TCR2. When TCR1 has a long conduction time, C2 charges
negatively during a small part of the cycle, so that a shorter recharge
time is required to fire TCR2 in the next half cycle. The use of two
controlled rectifiers in this circuit provides full-wave control of the
power supplied to the lamp. When controlled rectifier TCR1 or TCR2
is conducting, the dimmer circuit is effectively shorted by them, and
the entire supply voltage is dropped across the lamp. B is a half-wave
circuit.

INDUCTION TRANSCEIVER

A set of two of these transceivers is useful for short-range com-
munications or code practice. With the key of one unit held closed,
a tone will be heard in both pairs of earphones each time the other key
is closed. The induction transceiver has a range of only a few yards,
but with an added transistor audio amplifier you can increase its range
considerably. Each transceiver is an ultrasonic oscillator functioning
also as a heterodyne detector. The inductive field of each loop is coupled to the other loop, inducing signals in it. A suitable loop can be
wound on an 18-inch diameter, 5/8-inch high cylinder. The collector
coil (L1) should consist of 5 turns of number 12 to number 20 wire
and the emitter coil L2 consists of one turn. The turns should be

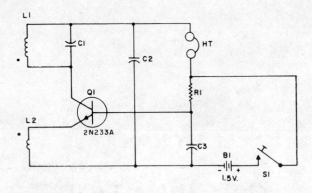

B1 - 1.5V. Battery Burgess #2R or equivalent
C1 - .005 Mfd. Paper Capacitor.
C2, C3 - .02 Mfd. Paper Capacitor.
HT - Earphones, approximately 2000Ω.

L1, L2 - See text.
Q1 - Sylvania 2N233A Transistor.
R1 - 47K 1/2w. Resistor.
S1 - Telegraph Key preferably with circuit closing switch.

Courtesy of Sylvania Electric Products, Inc.

Induction-transceiver circuit.

spaced about 1/8 inch between centers. These dimensions are not critical, but the tank circuits must be very nearly identical for the tone to be heard. The rest of the circuit can be mounted on or in the coil support.

When key S1 is depressed, the oscillator circuit is biased into conduction. As the current increases on the collector of Q1, a magnetic field is developed around L1 and is coupled to coil L2. The resulting voltage developed on the emitter of Q1 drives it further into conduction until it eventually reaches saturation. As the transistor reaches saturation, the magnetic field around L1 collapses, and a reverse bias is developed at the emitter of Q1. Q1 now decreases conduction until it reaches cutoff. The oscillator is now ready for the next cycle.

This all happens very quickly, resulting in an ultrasonic-frequency output. When two of these units are placed close together, the coupling of the two coils produces a mixing of the signals in each transceiver; an audible difference frequency is then heard in the earphones.

To increase the range, replace the headphones by a 2,200-ohm resistor, and connect the collector side of this resistor to the input of a transistor audio amplifier having the headphones connected to its output. With such an amplifier the output is sufficient to operate a transistorized relay for door-opening or other remote-control purposes. If you are unable to get a tone, reverse the connections to either L1 or L2, but not both.

191

OSCILLATORS

POWER OSCILLATORS

This circuit is a single-transistor power-oscillator operated from a 6-volt source; it can produce about 1 watt in the frequency range between 50 and 60 kc, and it may be used for a variety of purposes. L2 is a radio-frequency choke consisting of about 100 turns of No. 30 enamelled wire wound on a 3/8-inch diameter form with a winding length of 1/2-inch. The value of L1 should be about 20 microhenrys; it may be constructed with about 33 turns of No. 18 wire on a 1 3/4-inch coil form having a winding length of about 3 1/2 inches. This coil has a low value of inductance; therefore C1 and C2 must have rather large values. Control R3 is used for bias adjustment, and the circuit may be loaded by tapping off a portion of inductor L1 or using a few

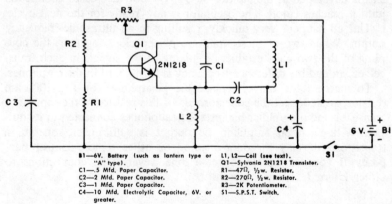

B1—6V. Battery (such as lantern type or "A" type).
C1—.5 Mfd. Paper Capacitor.
C2—2 Mfd. Paper Capacitor.
C3—1 Mfd. Paper Capacitor.
C4—10 Mfd. Electrolytic Capacitor, 6V. or greater.

L1, L2—Coil (see text).
Q1—Sylvania 2N1218 Transistor.
R1—47Ω, ½w. Resistor.
R2—270Ω, ½w. Resistor.
R3—2K Potentiometer.
S1—S.P.S.T. Switch.

Courtesy of Sylvania Electric Products, Inc.

Power-oscillator circuit.

turns as a secondary for L1. A check may be made in the circuit by connecting a No. 40 or 47 pilot lamp across this inductor.

HIGH-POWER PULSE GENERATOR WITH DUAL OUTPUT

This circuit uses a gate turn-off switch (GTO), a General Electric ZJ-224, which is a 3-terminal, PNPN silicon device for power switching. This device can handle as much as 2 amperes of current with blocking voltages up to 400 volts. The GTO can be turned on or off by signals of the proper polarity applied to its input-gate terminal.

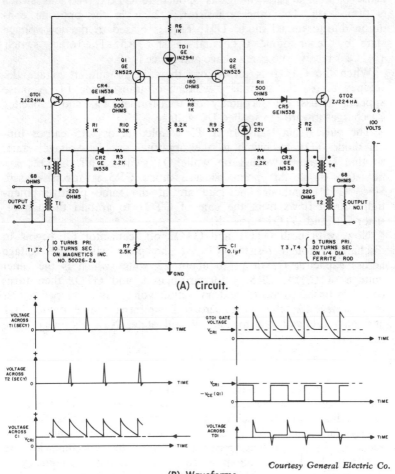

(A) Circuit.

(B) Waveforms.
High-power pulse generator.

This specific circuit was designed to produce two outputs, each of which is a series of pulses for use in high-frequency or high-power inverters. The two outputs are electrically isolated, and each produces a train of 1 ampere, 5 microsecond pulses into 20-ohm loads. The 180° phase difference between the outputs is maintained by use of a single timing network consisting of resistor R7 and capacitor C1. The output frequency is variable over a range of 1,000 to 20,000 cps by adjustment of resistor R7.

As shown, the supply voltage is 100 volts, and there are two individual outputs from transformers T1 and T2. Initially Q1 is biased on through resistors R8, R11, R2, and diode CR5. Because of this, a gate voltage is applied to GTO1, and this switch is turned on. The other transistor, Q2, is in the opposite condition due to tunnel diode TD1; TD1 is biased to the low-voltage state by zener diode CR1 and resistor R5. The other switch (GTO2) receives no gate voltage and hence is off.

When the GTO1 is turned on, there is an output voltage developed across the secondary winding of transformer T1. A pulse appears across the secondary of transformer T3, and capacitor C1 charges toward the applied DC voltage.

The pulse from transformer T3 coupled across R5 causes tunnel diode TD1 to switch to the opposite, or high-voltage, state, so that Q2 now switches on while Q1 switches off. GTO2 cannot turn on at this point because diode CR5 is reverse-biased. Since GTO1 cathode and gate are at the same positive potential, current flows from the gate of GTO1 to ground through resistor R1, and GTO1 turns off.

Now, with both GTO1 and GTO2 off, capacitor C1 begins to discharge through resistor R7. At the point where the voltage across capacitor C1 drops to about 22 volts (which is the zener voltage of CR1), CR5 is forward-biased, and GTO2 then turns on. This process repeats, and an output voltage is developed across transformer T2; the pulse across T4 returns tunnel diode TD1 and also Q1 and Q2 to the original state. Now the next cycle can start.

THEREMIN

The theremin is an electronic musical instrument that is capable of producing clear, variable musical tones. The theremin has two radio-frequency oscillators adjusted to frequencies that are nearly the same, differing only by a low audio frequency. When received on a broadcast receiver, both of these frequencies are detected. In the detection process the difference frequency is developed and amplified as an audible tone. A hand near inductor L1 or L2 changes the capacitance in the tank circuit and

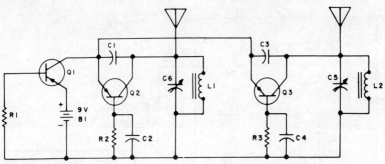

B1 — 9-volt battery
C1, C3 — 200 mmfd disc ceramic or mica
C2, C4 — 0.01 mfd, disc ceramic or paper
C5, C6 — 0-200 mmfd trimmer capacitors

L1, L2 — ferrite loop antenna
Q1 — Sylvania 2N1265 transistor
Q2, Q3 — Sylvania 2N1264 transistor
R1 — 180 k, ½ w
R2, R3 — 47 k, ½ w
Courtesy Sylvania Electric Products, Inc.

Theremin circuit.

shifts the frequency at which the circuit oscillates. If the frequency of only one of the oscillators is changed, a difference frequency is generated in the broadcast receiver, resulting in an increase or decrease in the pitch of the audible tone.

Transistor Q2 is a radio-frequency oscillator. Inductor L1 and capacitor C6 form a tuned tank in the collector circuit of Q2. Inductor L1 is adjusted so that it resonates with capacitor C6 at the radio frequency desired (near the center of the broadcast band). Transistor Q3 is an independent radio-frequency oscillator. Inductor L2 and capacitor C5 form a tuned tank in the collector circuit of Q3 similar to L1 and C6 in the collector circuit of Q2. Capacitors C1 and C2 and resistor R2 provide feedback and bias for transistor Q2. Similarly, capacitors C3 and C4 and resistor R4 provide feedback and bias for transistor Q3. Transistor Q1 provides DC current for the oscillators at an impedance level that is adequate to mix the oscillator outputs.

To operate the theremin, tune a standard AM broadcast receiver near the middle of the dial. Adjust L1 until a whistling sound is heard. Tune L2 until a squealing sound is heard. Adjust the tuning of the broadcast receiver to obtain the lowest tone possible. The theremin is now ready for playing. Simply move your hand near either of the inductors, and the tone changes.

BOAT HORN

The boat horn is a compact sounding device that can be heard from a great distance and has a variety of uses other than as a boat horn. The boat horn is basically a free running multivibra

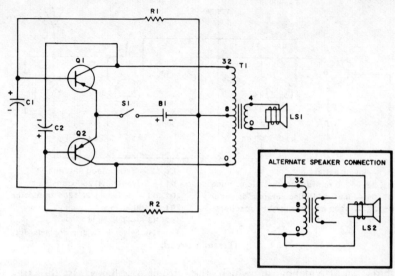

B1 — 12-volt battery (1 ampere drain) conventional auto or boat battery, or 2 Burgess F4P1 batteries wired in series.
C1, C2 — 2.0 mfd, electrolytic, 25-volt
LS1 — 8-ohm tweeter, Lafayette HK-3 or equivalent*
Q1, Q2 — Sylvania 2N307 power transistor

R1, R2 — 220 Ω, 1 w
S1 — single-pole, single-throw pushbutton switch, normally open
T1 — Lafayette TR-94 or equivalent
*LS2 for alternate connection — 45 ohm paging trumpet; University CMIL-45, University MIL-45, or equivalent

Courtesy Sylvania Electric Products, Inc.

Boat-horn circuit.

tor that is also used as a power output stage. It may be used in conjunction with burglar- and fire-alarm systems as well as other sounding systems. If the horn is used outdoors, it is desirable to use a speaker designed to withstand the weather. Paging trumpets, commonly used in mobile announcing rigs, are ideal. If the horn is used indoors, an ordinary hi-fi tweeter is adequate. The speaker should be connected to the terminals on the output transformer that have an impedance half that of the speaker. An alternate connection for 48-ohm paging trumpets is shown.

The free-running multivibrator, composed of transistors Q1 and Q2, is also the power-output stage. If transistor Q1 fires, its collector voltage rises with respect to the negative battery terminal. The sudden rise in voltage is coupled through capacitor C2 to the base of transistor Q2, back-biasing Q2 into cutoff. At cut-off the collector voltage on Q2 drops to the negative battery potential. The negative-going voltage is coupled through capacitor C1 to the base of Q2, causing Q1 to conduct more heavily. Transistor Q1 continues conducting until the base voltage of Q2 is low enough for conduction to start again, thus completing one cycle. The triggering process is now repeated with Q2 cutting off Q1.

When constructing the boat horn, it is necessary to provide good heat sinks for the two transistors. Heat sinks 1-1/2 × 2-1/2 inches made from 1/16-inch aluminum are adequate. The heat sinks must be electrically insulated from each other and from the rest of the circuit, since the collectors of these transistors are tied to the case and hence to the heat sinks.

HIGH-VOLTAGE SAWTOOTH GENERATOR

This circuit uses the gated turn-off switch as a sawtooth generator in conjunction with a zener diode. This is a free-running, high-voltage, sawtooth generator operating at approximately 75 kc. Applying power to theh circuit from the 400-volt source causes the transistor switch to trigger and connect the power supply across

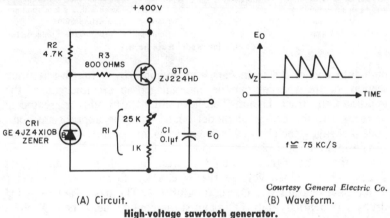

Courtesy General Electric Co.

(A) Circuit.   (B) Waveform.

High-voltage sawtooth generator.

capacitor C1. When the voltage on the switch gate rises above the avalanche voltage of zener diode CR1, current through resistor R3 reverses, and the gated turn-off switch turns off. Capacitor C1 then discharges through R1; this resistor is a combination of the 25K control in series with the 1K resistor. After capacitor C1 discharges, the switching device again turns on and repeats the cycle.

MODEL-TRAIN HORN

The model-train horn is a must for model-train enthusiasts. The horn is composed of a flip-flop, or multivibrator, circuit that generates the horn signal and an audio amplifier. The circuit can be

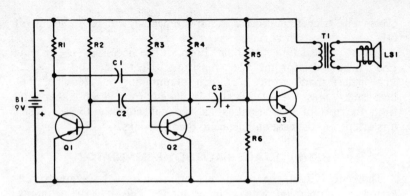

Circuit for model-train horn.

built into one of the train cars and operated by a fourth-rail track section, or the speaker can be camouflaged in secondary near the middle of the track layout. The horn circuit also adds a great deal of realism to the action of model boats; with the appropriate component changes, the circuit will create a foghorn sound.

The multivibrator circuit composed of transistors Q1 and Q2 generates the horn signal. When Q1 fires, its collector voltage rises sharply. The sudden voltage rise is coupled through capacitor C1 to the base of transistor Q2, cutting off Q2. The base voltage on Q2 drops exponentially until Q2 again starts conducting. When Q2 fires, its collector voltage rises sharply. The sudden voltage rise is coupled through capacitor C2 to the base of Q1, completing the cycle. Resistors R1 and R4 are collector load resistors. Resistors R2 and R3 provide base bias for Q1 and Q2 respectively. The horn signal from the collector of Q2 is coupled through capacitor C3 to the base of audio amplifier Q3. The horn signal is amplified by Q3 and coupled through transformer T1 to speaker LS1. Resistors R5 and R6 provide base bias for Q3. The primary winding of transformer T1 is the collector load for Q3.

The parts list gives a value of 0.02 mfd for capacitors C1 and C2. Capacitors having this value will produce a sound very much like that of a diesel. To produce a sound similar to a foghorn, use a value of 0.033 mfd. For higher pitched sounds, any capacitor value down to 0.0047 mfd may be used.

CONTROLLED-RECTIFIER OSCILLATOR

The controlled-rectifier oscillator in circuit A is a self-oscillating pulse generator. The fast switching time and the high current capability of controlled rectifiers make them ideal for this type of oscillator circuit. With the proper selection of component values, this circuit could be used as an audio oscillator or as a gating circuit with an electronic switch.

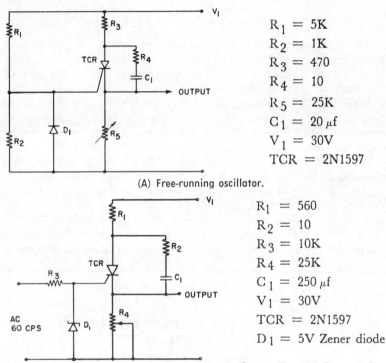

$R_1 = 5K$
$R_2 = 1K$
$R_3 = 470$
$R_4 = 10$
$R_5 = 25K$
$C_1 = 20\ \mu f$
$V_1 = 30V$
$TCR = 2N1597$

(A) Free-running oscillator.

$R_1 = 560$
$R_2 = 10$
$R_3 = 10K$
$R_4 = 25K$
$C_1 = 250\ \mu f$
$V_1 = 30V$
$TCR = 2N1597$
$D_1 = 5V$ Zener diode

Courtesy Transitron Electronic Corp.

(B) Synchronized oscillator.
Controlled-rectifier – oscillator circuits.

The 30-volt DC input is applied across voltage-dividing resistors R1 and R2, providing a 5-volt bias voltage at the gate of controlled rectifier TCR. Diode D1 prevents the bias voltage from going negative. At the same time a current starts flowing through resistors R3 and R4, capacitor C1, and frequency-adjust potentiometer R5. Gradually the voltage drop across resistor R5 decreases as the voltage across capacitor C1 approaches the 30-volt supply voltage. As soon as the cathode voltage on the TCR decreases from a high positive value to the predetermined gate voltage of approximately 5 volts, the TCR switches on, and C1 discharges through the TCR and resistor R4. Resistor R4 protects the TCR from excessive current when C1 is discharging. After C1 discharges, the TCR switches off, and the circuit is ready to start another cycle. Adjustment of frequency-adjust potentiometer R5 varies the charge time of capacitor C1 and the frequency of the output signal. A time variation from 0.6 to 0.04 seconds can be obtained with the component values given in the parts list. Circuit B shows a synchronized oscillator.

BLOCKING OSCILLATOR

The blocking oscillator in this circuit is capable of producing a variable pulse-output frequency between 70 and 340 kc. The pulse width is variable from 1.5 to 13.0 microseconds with a rise time of less than 60 nanoseconds and a fall time of less than 150 nanoseconds. At 70 kc, the output of this blocking oscillator circuit is approximately 3.7 volts. At 340 kc, the output voltage drops to approximately 1.3 volts. The time between pulses is controlled by capacitor C2. The pulse width is controlled by resistor R_p.

When voltage is applied to the circuit, transistor Q1 is biased into conduction, increasing its collector current. A voltage is induced in the base winding of the transformer which produces current to drive the transistor into cutoff. This sudden collector current increase and decrease results in a sharp, rectangular pulse at the emitter. The 1:1 pulse transformer produces a large reverse bias on the base-emitter diode; this results in shorter transition times than are possible with

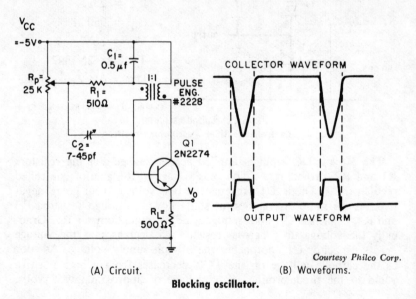

(A) Circuit.   (B) Waveforms.

Courtesy Philco Corp.

Blocking oscillator.

other turns ratios. By raising the supply voltage, the pulse width is increased, since this voltage controls the base bias through R_p and R1.

TRANSISTORIZED ORGAN

The transistorized organ consists of an audio-frequency oscillator, or tone generator, a speaker to provide sound output, and a small keyboard for selecting the various notes. This instrument plays only one note at a time. If more than one key is pressed at the same time, the note is produced by the key that is electrically nearest capacitor C6. The combination of capacitors C1 through C6 was chosen to approximate the musical scale. If you wish to tune the organ, a slightly smaller value may be used for C1 through C6 and a small trimmer capacitor placed in parallel with each. The organ may now

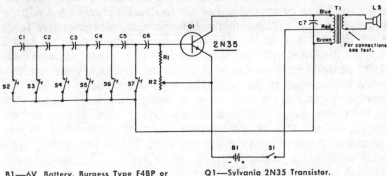

B1—6V. Battery, Burgess Type F4BP or equivalent.
C1 through C7—Capacitor, 0.02 mfd., Paper or Ceramic Disc Type 12V. or greater.
LS—Permanent Magnet Loudspeaker, 5 or 6 inch.

Q1—Sylvania 2N35 Transistor.
R1—470 ohm, ½w. Resistor.
R2—100K Potentiometer.
S1—S.P.S.T. Switch.
S2 through S7—Switches or keys. (See Text).
T1—Transformer, Stancor Type A-3856.

Courtesy Sylvania Electric Products, Inc.

Transistorized-organ circuit.

be tuned to any other instrument by adjusting the trimmer capacitors. Transistor Q1 is a grounded-emitter audio oscillator. Feedback for the oscillator is through the primary of transformer T1. Resistor R2 provides a variable bias for the oscillator and should be adjusted to set the frequency range of the instrument. The secondary of T1 provides the low-impedance output terminals for the voice coil of a PM speaker. Accurate matching of impedances between transformer and speaker is not important in this case. The combination of terminals that gives best results should be used.

The keyboard may be made from doorbell push buttons mounted on a suitable base board. If it is preferred, the keyboard may be made from brass strips approximately 1/4-inch wide and 1/32 inch thick. One brass strip serves as the common terminal for all keys The individual key switches S2 through S7 may then be mounted at right angles to the common strip.

PHASE-SHIFT OSCILLATOR

The phase-shift oscillator is essentially a current amplifier with a current-feedback network that produces a 180° phase-shift from collector to base. The amplifier, usually a common-emitter type, provides sufficient gain to overcome the losses in the feedback network. With the proper selection of RC feedback values, a wide range of frequencies can be obtained. The parts list gives values for constructing a 1 kc or a 15 kc phase-shift oscillator.

Resistor R1 provides a variable base bias for the transistor. R1 is set so that the base bias is just high enough to sustain oscillations; that is, the current gain of the transistor is equal to, or slightly greater than, the losses or attenuation of the feedback network. A feedback signal from the collector to the base provides a regenerative feedback signal. Since, in the common-emitter configuration, the signal between base and collector is reversed 180° in phase, an additional 180° phase shift is necessary to make the feedback signal positive when it is applied to the base. This is accomplished by an RC network consisting of six sections, each contributing a 30° phase shift at the frequency of oscillation. Resistor R3 is a DC biasing resistor for the emitter. The 10 mfd capacitor across R3 is the emitter bypass capacitor. Resistor R_L is the collector load. The output of the phase-shift oscillator is taken from the wiper arm of R_L and coupled through a capacitor for DC isolation. The output waveform of the

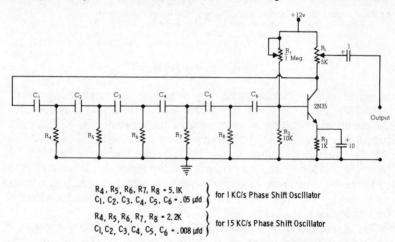

R4, R5, R6, R7, R8 = 5.1K
C1, C2, C3, C4, C5, C6 = .05 μfd } for 1 KC/s Phase Shift Oscillator

R4, R5, R6, R7, R8 = 2.2K
C1, C2, C3, C4, C5, C6 = .008 μfd } for 15 KC/s Phase Shift Oscillator

Courtesy Sylvania Electric Products, Inc.

Phase-shift – oscillator circuit.

phase-shift oscillator is nearly sinusoidal. The output frequency is fixed; that is, with fixed resistance and capacitance in the phase-shifting network, the 180° phase shift occurs at only one frequency. At other frequencies, the capacitive reactance increases or decreases, causing a variation in phase relationship. The feedback is then degenerative, preventing sustained oscillations. The phase-shift oscillator can be made variable by using ganged variable capacitors or resistors in the phase-shift network.

BLOCKING OSCILLATOR

The blocking oscillator may be considered as a one-stage amplifier with regenerative feedback coupling. Resistance R1 and capacitor C1 are significant in determining the repetition rate of the blocking oscillator. There are two sets of component values given in the parts list. With the 2N404 transistor, a 10-mc signal with a pulse width of 40 nanoseconds, a rise time of 20 nanoseconds and a fall time of 20 nanoseconds is obtained. With the 2N781 transistor, a 2.83-mc signal with a pulse width of 340 nanoseconds, a rise time of 58 nanoseconds, and a fall time of 45 nanoseconds is obtained.

When the circuit is energized, current rises rapidly in the base due to the forward bias established between the base and emitter. Current in the collector circuit increases, inducing a voltage in transformer winding 3-6. This voltage charges capacitor C through the small forward resistance of the base-emitter diode and appears across this resistance, increasing the forward bias. The charge on capacitor C continues to build up regeneratively, causing the transistor to switch on. Diode D2 clamps the collector-to-base voltage to 1 volt; this reduces the switching time. Diode D1 prevents the high peak-inverse flyback voltage from appearing across the collector-to-base diode; hence, D1 prevents transistor damage. When D2 is conducting,

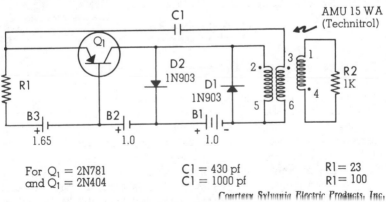

For Q_1 = 2N781 and Q_1 = 2N404

C1 = 430 pf
C1 = 1000 pf

R1 = 23
R1 = 100

Courtesy Sylvania Electric Products, Inc.

Blocking-oscillator circuit.

203

the magnetizing inductance of the transformer is in parallel with voltage from battery B1. The current in the inductor builds up in magnitude until it is sufficient to cancel the current in the diode. As a result, D2 opens, and the collector voltage increases in magnitude until it reaches the combined voltage of batteries B1 and B2. When the collector voltage reaches this point, diode D1 prevents any further change in the collector voltage, and the energy stored in the magnetizing inductance discharges through D1. Since during the pulse capacitor C1 stores a charge, the emitter is biased off until C1 discharges sufficiently to allow the transistor to be forward-biased. The cycle is now completed. The output pulse is coupled through the transformer to the external load (R2).

CONTROLLED-RECTIFIER RELAXATION OSCILLATOR

This circuit is a low-frequency, controlled-rectifier, relaxation oscillator suitable for triggering high-power controlled rectifiers used in inverters, ring counters, and other applications. The frequency of the oscillator ranges from about 2 kc to one pulse in two minutes. The circuit is, therefore, well suited for operation as a delay timer.

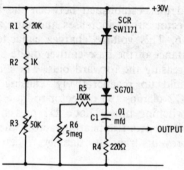

Circuit of controlled-rectifier relaxation oscillator.

When voltage is applied to the relaxation oscillator, current flows through resistors R1, R2, and R3. The voltage developed at the junction of R1 and R2 is sufficient to trigger the controlled rectifier (SCR) on. A pulse appears across resistor R4 and capacitor C starts charging to the supply voltage (minus the forward voltage drop across the diode and controlled rectifier). Provided that the effective parallel resistance of resistors R3 and R5-R6 does not permit the flow of the minimum holding current, the controlled rectifier will turn off when capacitor C is charged to a sufficiently high voltage. The diode now becomes reverse-biased, and capacitor C begins to discharge through R5 and R6. When capacitor C discharges to a sufficiently low voltage, the controlled rectifier is again triggered on, and another pulse appears across resistor R4. The cycle is now completed. The frequency of the relaxation oscillator depends on the resistance R2, R3, R5, and R6 and the capacitance of C. Silicon-controlled rectifiers of low power ratings are usable in low-frequency relaxation oscillators that periodically trigger high-power, silicon-controlled rectifiers.

UJT PULSE GENERATOR

This versatile UJT circuit generates alternate pulses that may be used for alternate triggers in an electronic switch. The circuit consists of two unijunction-transistor (UJT), relaxation-oscillator circuits that are synchronized by capacitor C3.

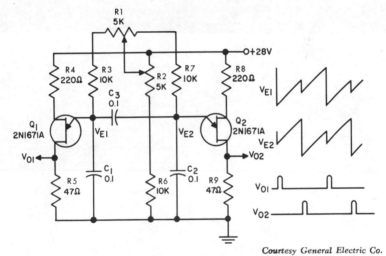

Courtesy General Electric Co.

UJT-pulse – generator circuit.

When power is applied to the circuit, capacitor C1 charges through resistors R1, R2, and R3. When the charge on C1 reaches the emitter-base 1 triggering level of unijunction transistor Q1, it discharges through resistor R5, developing a positive pulse at output V_{01}. Simultaneously, capacitor C2 starts charging through resistors R1, R2, and R7. When the charge on C2 reaches the emitter-base 1 triggering level of unijunction transistor Q2, it discharges through resistor R9, developing a positive pulse at output V_{02}. Each time one UJT fires, a negative voltage step is coupled to the emitter of the opposite UJT through C3. If this negative voltage step occurs when the emitter voltage is low, the delay in the firing of the UJT

205

will be less than if the step occurs when the emitter voltage is high, owing to the nonlinear charging characteristic of the capacitor. This produces the synchronization between the two oscillators.

The frequency of oscillation and the relative spacing between the pulses from the two outputs are controlled independently by potentiometers R2 and R1 respectively. For the circuit shown, the frequency can be adjusted between 200 cps and 800 cps, and the relative pulse spacing can be varied from 35% to 65%. The range of control of pulse spacing can be increased by reducing the size of C3 relative to C1 and C2. The size of C3 relative to C1 and C2 also determines the initial timing of the pulses when the power is first applied. If C3 is the same size as C1 and C2, the circuit will start with the same timing sequence that it has under steady state conditions (50% pulse spacing). This characteristic is very important for the reliable starting of parallel inverters.

SECTION 13

POWER CONVERTERS

DC-TO-DC CONVERTER

This efficient DC to DC converter combines the high efficiency of a switching-type regulator with good ripple reduction and the low output impedance of a series transistor regulator. You can vary the input voltage and the load current, and the output voltage remains constant at 24 volts.

When the input voltage is applied to the circuit, a fixed base bias is applied to GTO1 and Q1 from the cathodes of zener diodes CR3 and CR4 respectively. The positive bias on the base of GTO1 triggers it into conduction, producing a sudden increase in collector current. This increased collector current produces a mag-

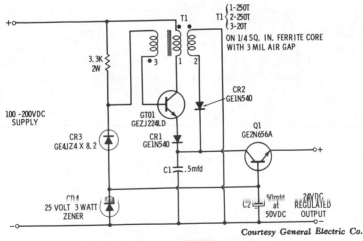

Courtesy General Electric Co.

Circuit for 100VDC to 24VDC converter.

207

netic field around winding 1 of transformer T1. The voltage developed in winding 3 of T1 biases GTO1 into saturation, at which time the collector current no longer increases, and the magnetic field around winding 1 of T1 starts to collapse. As the field collapses around T1, a negative bias is developed at the base of GTO1, holding it cut off until the field has completely collapsed. At this time the positive bias from zener diode CR3 again drives GTO1 into conduction. This repeating action results in an AC signal. The AC signal is coupled to winding 2 of T1 and rec-

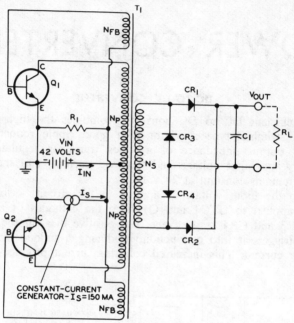

C: |1 μf

CR$_1$, CR$_2$, CR$_3$, CR$_4$: RCA-1N1763 silicon rectifiers

Q$_1$, Q$_2$: RCA-2N1490 high-power silicon transistors

R$_1$: 8 ohms

T: Core: ferrite toroid, Allen-Bradley Part No.T3750-107B, type RO3 material, or equivalent; primary: 44 turns No.14 wire, bifilar wound (N$_p$ = 22 turns): secondary (N$_S$) = 105 turns No.24 wire; feedback winding = 16 turns No.20 wire, bifilar wound (N$_{FB}$ = 8 turns)

Courtesy Radio Corporation of America.

Circuit for 42VDC to 200 VDC converter.

tified by diode CR2. Capacitor C1 filters the rectified voltage from T1. Series-regulator transistor Q1 provides current regulation for the 24-volt DC output.

42VDC-TO-200VDC CONVERTER

This circuit uses an input of 42 volts at 6.0 amperes and produces an output voltage of 200 volts at 0.97 amps with an efficiency of 77%. The transformer core is a ferrite toroid. The 3kc frequency minimizes the transformer turns without introducing large core-losses. As an inverter, rectifiers CR1 through CR4 and capacitor C1 are removed; under these conditions the output square wave has a peak-to-peak amplitude of about 400 volts.

120-WATT, DC-TO-DC CONVERTER

This 120-watt DC to DC converter uses a 28-volt, 5-ampere input to produce a 400-volt, 300-ma output. The circuit has a built-in, momentary short-circuit protection and a ripple output of 0.6 volts maximum. The 120-watt DC to DC converter generates a 10-kc signal from the 28-volt input, steps up the voltage through transformer T1, and rectifies and filters the 400-kc voltage to produce a 400-volt DC output.

Transistors Q1 and Q2 form the active part of a saturable-core square-wave oscillator. This type of circuit operates with greater efficiency and at higher frequencies than the mechanical vibrator

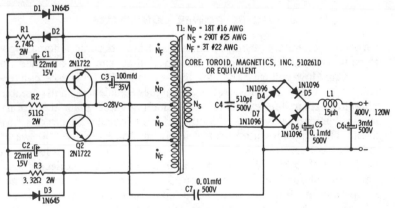

NOTES: 1. ALL RESISTANCE VALUES IN OHMS, 5% TOLERANCE.
2. ALL RESISTOR WATTAGE RATINGS AT 125°C AMBIENT.
3. CAPACITOR VOLTAGE RATINGS AT 125°C AMBIENT.
4. BOTH TRANSISTORS ON SAME HEAT SINK, θ_{C-HS} + θ_{HS-A} 4 C°/W EACH

Courtesy Texas Instruments, Inc.

Circuit for 120-Watt DC to DC converter.

normally found in portable power supplies. The transistors, functioning as switches, operate from cutoff to saturation. When the 28-volt source is applied between the collectors of the transistors and the center tap of the transformer, one of the transistors is driven into conduction, and the other is cut off. Assuming Q1 is conducting, the current through winding N_p of transformer T1 is coupled through winding N_f, diode D1, and capacitor C1 to the base of Q1. Q1 conducts heavily until the core of the transformer reaches saturation. At this time the bias is removed from the base of Q1. Transistor Q1 is now at cutoff, and its collector current ceases. Due to the collapsing field of the transformer windings, transistor Q1 is driven further into cutoff by the negative potential on its base, and transistor Q2 is driven into conduction by the positive potential produced by the collapsing field of the transformer windings. Transistor Q1 is maintained at cutoff while transistor Q2 conducts heavily. Once saturation of the core is reached, the switching of transistor Q1 from cutoff to conduction and transistor Q2 from conduction to cutoff occurs. The cycle is now ready for repetition. The resulting 10-kc square-wave signal is coupled through transformer T1. The secondary voltage in T1 is slightly greater than 400 volts. The 400-volt, 10-kc square wave is rectified by full-wave, bridge-rectifier diodes D4 through D7. The rectified output is filtered by the LC filter network consisting of capacitors C5 and C6 and inductor L1. It is then applied to the output terminals. Capacitor C7 is an AC ground-return path.

DC-TO-DC POWER CONVERTERS

Power converters using transistors have become increasingly popular because of the high efficiency that can be obtained in converting low-voltage DC to high-voltage DC. These converters have a smaller physical size, higher efficiency, and greater reliability; their life expectancy is much greater than the rotary or mechanical converters. Eight different converter circuits are given. Their power-output range is from 15 watts to 500 watts, and the voltage output varies from a low of 100 volts to a maximum of 500 volts. These circuits can switch collector currents from about 1 ampere to about 25 amperes. They are designed to operate at 400 cps and 1000 cps. In each case the output voltage can be changed by increasing or decreasing the number of secondary turns on the transformer.

The basic converter is the type A, which has two switching transistors and a transformer that has a square loop hysteresis curve. A voltage unbalance in the circuit causes one of the

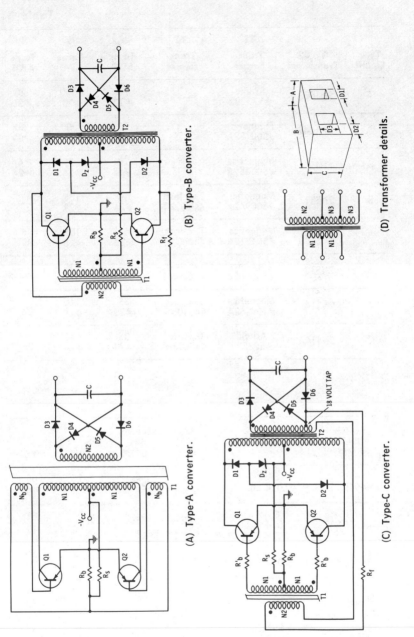

(A) Type-A converter.

(B) Type-B converter.

(C) Type-C converter.

(D) Transformer details.

Circuits for DC to DC power converters.

211

Table 1.

Type Circuit	Q1, Q2 Transistors	T1 Transformer	T2 Transformer	N_1 Turns AWG	N_2 Turns AWG	N_b Turns AWG
A	2N1038	Arnold #5772D2	——	70 #18	1800 #30	20 #30
A	2N1042	Magnetics #500172A	——	78 #16	2000 #29	30 #29
A	2N456	Magnetics #500352A	——	29 #17	275 #24	6 #24
B	2N511	Magnetics #500942A	Tex. Inst. 440402-1	48 #24	185 #28	——
B	2N512	Magnetics #501812A	Tex. Inst. 440404-1	48 #22	185 #26	——
B	2N513	Magnetics #500262A	Tex. Inst. 440406-1	35 #20	140 #26	——
B	2N514	Magnetics #500262A	Tex. Inst. 440408-1	35 #20	140 #24	——
C	2N514A	Arnold #5233D2	Tex. Inst. 440413-1	35 #20	140 #24	——

Table 2.

TRANSFORMER NUMBER	LAMINATIONS	PRIMARY TURNS	SECONDARY TURNS	TURNS LAYERS PRI.	TURNS LAYERS SEC.
TI 440402-1	EI-12 0.014 SIL.	42	595	14 / 3	66 / 10
TI 440404-1	EI-12 0.014 SIL.	42	955	14 / 3	81 / 12
TI 440406-1	EI-125 0.014 SIL.	28	383	7 / 4	55 / 7
TI 440408-1	EI-125 0.014 SIL.	28	623	7 / 4	63 / 10
TI 440413-1	EI-175 0.014 SIL.	32	191	11 / 3	38 / 5

Parts List

R_b or R'_b ohms	R_s ohms	R_r ohms	D_z Zener Diode	D1, D2 Diodes	D3, D4 D5, D6 Diodes	C μf	Rating watts
15	1200	—	——	——	1N2071	2	15
15	1500	—	——	——	1N2071	4	30
5	180	—	——	——	1N2071	6	55
2	100	5	1N1817	1N2069	1N2071	10	100
2	75	10	1N1817	1N2069	1N2071	20	150
1	75	5	1N1817	1N2069	1N2071	20	200
1	75	5	1N1817	1N2069	1N2071	30	250
$R_b = \frac{1}{2}$ $R'_b = \frac{1}{2}$	75	10	1N1825	1N2069	1N1126	40	500

Transformer Specifications

PRI. WIRE SIZE INCLUDES BIFILAR DESIGNATION, IF ANY	SECONDARY WIRE SIZE	A	B	C	D_1	D_2	D_3
#14 Fx	#26	1"	3"	2½"	½"	½"	1½"
#14 Fx	#28	1"	3"	2½"	½"	½"	1½"
#13 Fx BIFILAR	#22	1¼"	3¾"	3⅛"	⅝"	⅝"	1⅞"
#13 Fx BIFILAR	#24	1 ³⁄₁₆"	3¾"	3⅛"	⅝"	⅝"	1⅞"
#12 Fx BIFILAR	#16	1¾"	5¼"	4⅜"	⅞"	⅞"	2⅝"

transistors to conduct a small amount of current. Because of the circuit arrangement there is a regeneration that turns off the second transistor while the first one is driven into saturation. When the magnetic core becomes saturated, the collector current increases rapidly, since it is limited only by the resistance in the collector circuit and, of course, the transistor characteristics. After the core is saturated, the induced voltage in the winding is zero, and the resulting lack of base drive causes the first transistor to turn off so that the collector current drops to zero. This drop in collector current causes the polarity in all of the windings to change. This biases the first transistor off, and the second transistor on.

For converters which require a power output of more than 55 watts, two transformers of the type shown in circuit B are used. Here only the small transformer (T1) will saturate, and the extra current necessary at saturation is very small compared to the load current. This circuit arrangement allows the use of a small drive transformer of the square-loop variety to drive a larger, more inexpensive power transformer that steps up the output voltage to the required value. With the supply voltage connected as shown, one of the transistors (say Q1) conducts, causing the collector voltage to drop to almost zero. A voltage is built up across the primary of the output transformer and is applied to the primary of the drive transformer by means of a feedback resistor (R_f). The secondary windings keep transistor Q2 biased off while transistor Q1 is biased into conduction. When the core of this driver transformer reaches saturation, increasing current causes a greater voltage drop across the feedback resistor. This greater voltage drop aids the regenerative action which switches Q2 on and Q1 off. Transistor Q2 then remains on until reverse saturation of the transformer is reached; then the entire circuit switches back to its original state, and the cycle is repeated. Frequency is a function of the design of the smaller or saturating transformer (T1) and the feedback resistor. Collector current for the conducting transistor increases to the total of the primary load current and the current needed to magnetize the output transformer and the feedback current required to produce the drive. Magnetizing current for the output transformer is only a portion of the rated output current. This is due to the fact that the output transformer does not saturate.

Table 1 is the parts list for the three different types of circuits shown. Specifications for the output transformer (T2) shown in Types B and C may be obtained from Table 2 and part D of the illustration.

214

6VDC-TO-12VDC CONVERTER

This DC to DC converter provides a 12-volt DC output capable of delivering 1 ampere from a 6-volt input. The circuit employs two transistors (Q1 and Q2) as an oscillator circuit and two transistor (Q3 and Q4) connected in a diode configuration. The 12-volt output from the emitters of Q3 and Q4 may be filtered by capacitor C1 and bleeder resistor R3.

When the 6-volt source is applied to the circuit, transistors Q1 and Q2 are forward-biased, but due to component variations one will conduct more heavily. Assuming Q1 starts to conduct more heavily than Q2, the increasing collector current of Q1 produces a magnetic field in the core of transformer T1. T1 then produces a voltage on the secondary winding (B). The po-

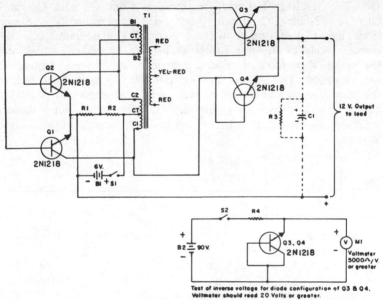

Test of inverse voltage for diode configuration of Q3 & Q4.
Voltmeter should read 20 Volts or greater.

B1—6 Volt Automobile Battery or equivalent capable of supplying 2 Amperes.
B2—90 Volt "B" Battery, Burgess #N60 (with snap terminals) or equivalent.
C1—1000 Mfd. Electrolytic Capacitor, 15V. or greater.
M1—Voltmeter, 100V. D.C., 5000ΩN. or greater.
Q1, Q2, Q3, Q4—Sylvania 2N1218 Transistor.
R1—30Ω ½w. Resistor.
R2—220Ω 1w. Resistor.
R3—330Ω 1w. Resistor.
R4—20K 1w. Resistor.
S1—S.P.S.T. Switch with low resistance contacts.
S2—S.P.S.T. Toggle Switch.
T1—Transformer, Triad TY68S.

Courtesy Sylvania Electric Products, Inc.

Circuit for 6VDC to 12VDC converter.

larity of the voltage across winding B is such that Q1 will be biased further into conduction, and Q2 will be biased to decrease conduction. This action continues until Q1 reaches saturation, and Q2 is cut off. At this time the magnetic field in winding B collapses, producing forward bias on Q2 and reverse bias on Q1. As the field collapses, Q1 is driven into cutoff, and Q2 begins to conduct. As Q2 increases conduction, a voltage is coupled from winding C to winding B. This increases conduction in Q2 until it reaches saturation, and decreases conduction in Q1 until it is cut off. At this time the field collapses, and the cycle is repeated. Proper polarity of the transformer windings must be observed; otherwise the circuit will not oscillate. The resulting square-wave signal is taken from the ends of winding C and applied to diode-connected transistors Q3 and Q4. The resulting full-wave rectification from Q3 and Q4 produces a 12-volt DC output. About one ampere may be drawn from the 12-volt output without exceeding maximum collector-current rating of the transistors. Transistors connected as Q3 and Q4 make very efficient diodes, provided the inverse voltage is not exceeded. This is not one of the measurements included in the transistor specifications, so the simple test shown in the schematic may be made to insure that Q3 and Q4 will function satisfactorily. These transistors should be mounted on a suitable heat sink.

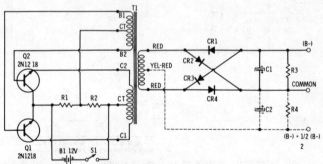

B1—12 Volt Automobile Battery or equivalent capable of supplying 1 Ampere.
C1, C2—8 Mfd. 450V. Electrolytic Capacitor.
CR1, CR2, CR3, CR4—Sylvania SR776 Diodes.
Q1, Q2—Sylvania 2N1218 Transistors.
R1—27Ω ½w. Resistor.
R2—300Ω 1w. Resistor.
S1—S.P.S.T. Switch with low resistance contacts.
T1—Transformer.

For (B+) 1	Use
250V.	Triad TY-68S
300V.	Triad TY-69S
325V.	Triad TY-70S

Courtesy Sylvania Electric Products, Inc.

Circuit for 12VDC to 300VDC converter.

12VDC-TO-300VDC CONVERTER

This DC to DC converter provides a high-voltage DC from a 12- to 14-volt source. T1 is a transformer having a rectangular hysteresis loop and is specially designed for this application. Transistors Q1 and Q2 oscillate at about 2 kc, producing square waves. Approximately 10 watts of power may be taken from the high-voltage output without exceeding the 1-ampere maximum collector-current rating of Q1 and Q2. The transistors should be mounted on a suitable heat sink.

Operation of the oscillator portion of this circuit is similar to that described for the preceding circuit. The resulting square-wave signal is taken from the secondary of T1 and rectified by full-wave rectifier diodes CR1 through CR4. The resulting high-voltage DC output is filtered by capacitor C1 and bleeder resistor R3. An output of half the voltage is shown by the dotted lines. If the second output is used, capacitor C2 and bleeder resistor R4 filter the output. Very little filtering is required since the output of the secondary is a square wave.

1-KC CHOPPER

This circuit is a DC chopper that operates at 1 kc and has a variable pulse-width control. The variable width control (R4) gives a continuous control of the pulse width from 10% to 90% of the operating period.

When power is applied to the circuit, capacitor C2 charges through resistor R1 until the emitter-base 1 voltage of unijunction transistor UJT1 exceeds the triggering level. At this time UJT1 fires, and capacitor C2 discharges through the primary winding of transformer T1 and resistor R3, producing a pulse that is coupled through T1, rectified by diodes CR1 through CR4, and applied to the gate of controlled rectifier SCR1. SCR1 is switched on, and current flows through the load, inductor L1, and the lower half of transformer T3. Resonant-charging action causes the voltage on capacitor C3 to rise above the supply voltage. Capacitor C3 discharges through resistors R4, R5, and R6, and capacitor C4, charging C4. When the charge on C4 becomes sufficient to trigger unijunction transistor UJT2, C4 discharges through T2, producing a pulse at the gate of SCR2, biasing SCR2 on. When SCR2 starts to conduct, the voltage at the cathode of SCR1 goes positive, switching SCR1 off, and current ceases to flow through the load. The charge time of C4, and thus the switching-off time of SCR1, is controlled by the setting of R4. Therefore, resistor R1 controls the frequency or pulse repetition rate, and resistor R4 controls the pulse width. SCR2 and

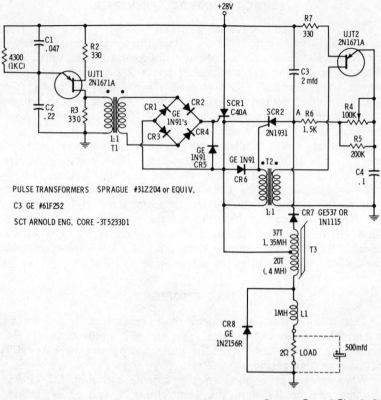

PULSE TRANSFORMERS   SPRAGUE #31Z204 or EQUIV.

C3 GE #61F252

SCT ARNOLD ENG. CORE -3T5233D1

Courtesy General Electric Co.

Circuit for 1-kc chopper.

the resonant charging circuit L1, T3, CR7, and C3 can be quite small since they carry only the turn-off energy.

DC CHOPPER

With this circuit, the current pulse-width to the load is more or less fixed by the time it takes the core of square-loop core autotransformer T2 to saturate, and the energy to the load can be varied with the trigger rate of controlled rectifier SCR1.

When power is applied to the circuit, capacitor C1 charges through resistors R1 and R2 until it reaches the triggering level of unijunction transistor UJT1. The trigger circuit uses UJT1 to drive transistor Q1 from cutoff to saturation. Since the energy in C1 is not used to trigger controlled rectifier SCR1, the smaller (.01 mfd) capacitor size can be used to obtain UJT operation to 20 kc. Resistor R5 limits the voltage amplitude of

218

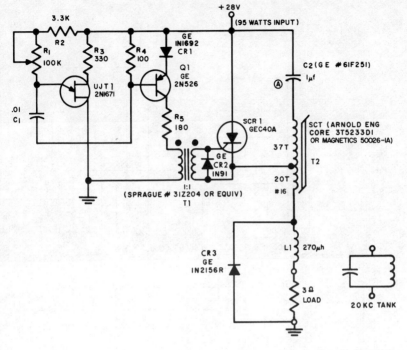

Courtesy General Electric Co.

Circuit for DC chopper.

the trigger pulse to SCR1. CR1 isolates the SCR turn-off pulse
from the UJT timing circuit.

Initially, point A is at zero potential. When SCR1 is triggered
the full line voltage appears across the 37-turn winding of
T2, quickly driving the core to negative saturation. When the
core saturates, the capacitor charges rapidly toward the supply
potential, and then the increasing load current starts driving the
core toward positive saturation. Between negative and positive
saturation, the core acts as a transformer, and C2 is charged
above the supply voltage to a potential determined by the load
current. When positive saturation is reached, the core again becomes essentially a short circuit, and the charged capacitor drives
the cathode of SCR1 above the anode voltage, thus switching it
off. Because of the circuit inductance, the voltage range at
point A varies from below ground potential in the interval before
SCR1 is fired to above the supply potential at SCR1 turnoff
time. The circuit operates with a pulse width of about 40 microseconds. The pulse width depends partly on the load and L1.

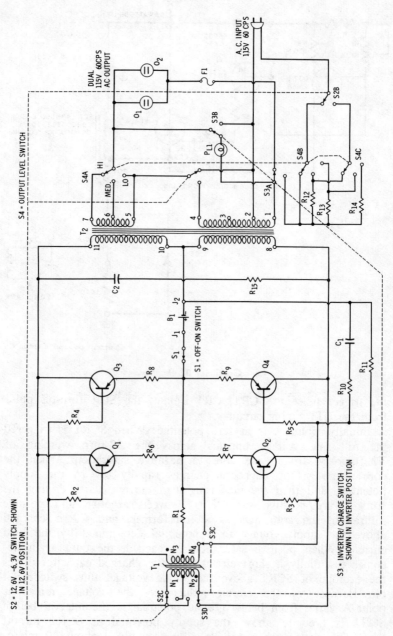

Courtesy of Minneapolis-Honeywell Regulator Co.

Inverter-charger circuit.

PARTS LIST

Q1, Q2, Q3 and Q4 = Honeywell DA2F2 Transistor

R1, R6, R7, R8 and R9 = 0.05 ohm Resistor (Each 6″ length of Balco Wire — B & S No. 19)

R2, R3, R4 and R5 = 0.5 ohm Resistor

R10 = 47 ohm Resistor

R11 = 330 ohm Resistor

R12 = 15 ohm — 75 watt Resistor

R13 = 50 ohm — 75 watt Resistor

R14 = 150 ohm — 50 watt Resistor

R15 = 15 ohm — 10 watt Resistor

C1 = 500mfd — 15 volt Capacitor

C2 = 30mfd — 25 volt non-polarized Capacitor

B1 = 6 or 12 VDC

P_{L1} = NE51H Neon Light with Dialco Type 931 H Pilot Light Assembly

S1 = SPST Toggle Switch (Cutler-Hammer 7501-K13 or equivalent)

S2 = 3PDT Slide Switch (Continental-Wirt G-369 or equivalent)

S3 = 4PDT Slide Switch (Stackpole SS-12 or equivalent)

S4 = 1 section, 3 pole, 3 position rotary switch (Mallory 1313L or equivalent)

T1 = Saturating Feedback Transformer MC-595

Windings	Core
N1, N2 = 328 Turns No. 24 Wire	5/16″ Stack of 50 DU
N3, N4 = 66 Turns No. 14 Wire	M7X .014″ Steel
	Laminations

T2 = Output transformer MC-594 (or Stancor RT-2012)

F1 = 3-amp Slo-Blo Fuse

J1 = Superior Binding Post (Red)

J2 = Superior Binding Post (Black)

O1 and O2 = Dual 115 Volt Outlet

Transformers T1 and T2 available from:

Mag-Con Engineering Company
2654 Kenzie Terrace
Minneapolis 18, Minnesota

INVERTER CHARGER

This is a portable, mobile, or marine 115-volt, 60-cycle AC power supply designed for a 6- or 12-volt operation. The circuit uses a 2-transformer, self excited, square-wave oscillator. Class B push-pull, common-emitter operation is used, and it is possible to reverse the operation so that the inverter may be used as a battery charger. The power output at 6-volts DC input is 125 watts. The power output at 12-volts DC input is 300 watts. The operating frequency is 60 cps with an output square wave at an efficiency of 75%.

INVERTER

This is a 200-watt, 60-cycle inverter that may be used as a portable line-voltage power supply. The circuit, as shown, is a 2-transformer, self-excited, square-wave oscillator. This circuit uses class B push-pull operation in a common-emitter configuration. The power output is 200 watts at 60 cps. The output voltage is 115-volts square-wave with an efficiency of 75%. This circuit may be used in the field to change the battery voltage to the ordinary alternating-current line voltage.

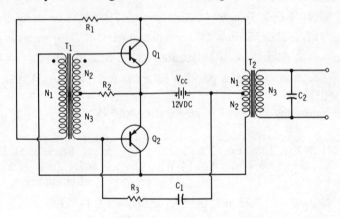

T_1 - Saturating feedback transformer

N_1 = 565 T #24 } Core = 3/8" stack
N_2, N_3 = 85 T #20 } 37 DU Orthonic

T_2 - Output Transformer

N_1, N_2 = 22 T #10 } Core = 2" stack
N_3 = 225 T #20 } 150 EI M7X steel

Q_1, Q_2 = Honeywell DA3F3 power transistors
R_1 = 20 ohms 10 w
R_2 = 2 ohms 2 watt
R_3 = 47 ohms
C_1 = 500μfd @ 25 VDC
C_2 = 0.5μfd @ 300 VAC

Courtesy of Minneapolis-Honeywell Regulator Co.

200-watt – inverter circuit.

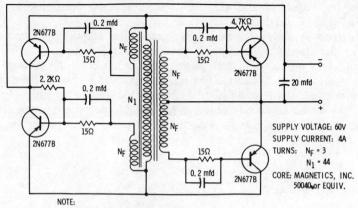

NOTE:
ALL RESISTORS ARE 2 WATT
THE NUMBER OF TURNS IN THE SECONDARY WINDING
IS DEPENDENT ON THE DESIRED OUTPUT VOLTAGE.

(A) Bridge-type circuit.

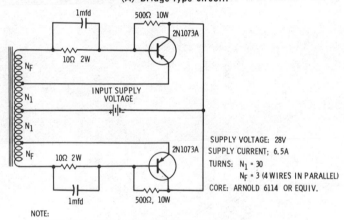

NOTE:
THE NUMBER OF TURNS IN THE SECONDARY WINDING
IS DEPENDENT ON THE DESIRED OUTPUT VOLTAGE.

Courtesy Bendix Corp.

(B) Push-pull circuit.
DC-to-DC — converter circuits.

DC-TO-DC CONVERTERS

Transistors have specific advantages for use as active switches in DC-to-DC converters. These advantages include high reliability, greater efficiency, and longer life as compared to the other means of switching for power conversion. These converters are limited only by the current ratings and the breakdown voltages of the transistors that are used. However, the switching transistors may be connected in parallel for a greater current

223

carrying capacity, and they may be connected in series to obtain higher breakdown voltages.

Circuit A shows a bridge-type circuit that allows input voltages near the transistor breakdown voltage. Four Bendix type 2N677B transistors are used in this circuit, which has a supply voltage of 60 volts at 4 amperes. The output power is taken from the transformer third-winding, and the output power of this circuit is 200 watts. Circuit B shows a push-pull type of converter. This uses a 28-volt supply voltage at 6.5 amperes. The power output is 150 watts.